Plants and Their
Economic Importance

Our
Plant
Resources

Frederick L. Fitzpatrick

Holt, Rinehart and Winston, Inc., New York

Frederick L. Fitzpatrick is Professor of Natural Sciences and Chairman of the Department of the Teaching of Natural Sciences at Teachers College, Columbia University. He is the author of several science textbooks, and is Director of the Science Manpower Project.

Copyright © 1964 by
HOLT, RINEHART AND WINSTON, INC.
Printed in the United States of America
12845-1914

Preface

About 15 centuries before the dawn of the Christian era, Queen Hatshepsut of Egypt sent an expedition to the Land of Punt to search for the "frankincense tree." Even before this venture, at least one Egyptian party had set forth on a similar expedition, for incense burning was an established custom in ancient Egypt, as well as in Asia.

The Land of Punt was Somali country of East Africa, where trees of the genus *Boswellia* grew. Other species of this genus were native to southern Asia. From these trees came frankincense, which like some other plant products gives off an odor or perfume when it is burned.

The Egyptians of 1500 B.C., or even 3000 B.C., were not the first people to exhibit an active concern about plants. As the reader will discover in the following pages, man has been partially dependent upon plants ever since the days of the primitive food gatherers who survived the last great ice age, propagated their kind and gave rise to modern man. Through this long interval of time human preoccupation with plants has never faltered, for the simple reason that plants are sources of food for man and other animals, as well as sources of fibers, adhesives, oils, drugs, and many other valuable materials.

The United States Department of Agriculture employs plant explorers who visit the far corners of the earth seeking plant varieties that may prove to have useful qualities. Hundreds of these varieties have been brought to the United States to be studied and tested. Modern plant explorers may come upon some wild or cultivated relative of a type we already raise, which happens to possess a special quality that is in demand. Perhaps this desired quality is resistance to some damaging plant disease, perhaps it is the ability to survive in a colder land, perhaps it is longer and stronger fibers in the plant stem, a root system of a particular type, or any one of a thousand other possibilities.

The "find" having been made, plant geneticists take over. The new variety with the desired quality is crossed with existing stock. Using the most modern principles of genetics, it may prove possible to develop a special, tailor-made plant, which combines the best features of both the old and the new.

In addition, some useful new plant species may still be found in nature. For example, a mold that proved invaluable as a source of one type of penicillin was discovered growing on a melon in Illinois only a few years ago.

Our ancestors used many plant products largely as they came from the field, forest, or sea. As time goes on, however, more and more of these products are transformed in modern factories, and emerge as a variety of substances that have little resemblance to the original materials. This is a very significant phase of human progress, because plants are not like coal or oil. Plants are renewable resources: when a new growing season comes along, we can raise more plants. On the other hand, when supplies of coal and oil are exhausted, millions of years must pass before natural processes will provide new sources.

In the following chapters, the reader will find discussions of many useful plant materials that come from the fields and forests, as well as from the seas. In general, the more important items have been emphasized, for it is impossible to include in these pages references to all of the plant materials that men use or have used.

Contents

1

The Plant World

Recent fossil discoveries in East Africa indicate that man-like creatures inhabited an ancient lake shore about one and three-quarter million years ago. Such predecessors of modern man were without doubt food gatherers, and it is probable that they or their descendants had primitive stone tools which were probably used in their foraging efforts. The ancestry of man goes back to before the time when large areas of the earth's surface were covered by the ice sheets of the Pleistocene.

Long after the great glaciers had melted, our human predecessors were still most concerned about three things: food, shelter, and survival. These primitive men, like those who preceded them, lived by food gathering, which means that they hunted, fished, and sought various plant products that nature provided. It was only in relatively recent times that a more stable mode of life was achieved.

Even our more remote ancestors undoubtedly had a very real interest in plants, because it was an interest spurred by necessity. They depended upon plants for foods, for materials used in building shelters, and at a later period, for substances used in making fabrics. At some long forgotten time they also turned to plant materials in their early, halting efforts to combat diseases.

The evidence at hand indicates that men entered North America via the Siberian route more than 300 centuries ago. Their descendants spread down through the Americas, where they learned to use plants that were not available to men of the old world. The beginnings of cultivation, both in the old world and the new, often extend so far back in time that we can only speculate as to where and when they took place. Ancient stores of wheat, barley, and millet have been unearthed in the towns along the shores of Swiss lakes where men lived during the late stone age. Clearly, the inhabitants of these early settlements had already begun to establish an agriculture.

Today, there are some human societies in which the people are still in a food-gathering stage of culture. But such societies tend to vanish, or to be superseded by societies having a more complex mode of existence. Meanwhile, the more progressive, early societies handed down to us a good many cultivated plants, and using modern knowledge of genetics and selection, we have been able to improve some of these plants substantially. But it is also true that we have so far found no real substitute for them. Some day men may have an effective process for synthesizing foods, and research is now proceeding along such lines. It has been found possible, for example, to put the chloroplasts (bodies which contain chlorophyll) of plant cells in a test tube along with inorganic phosphates, carbon dioxide, and water, to supply the energy of sunlight, and to obtain sugar. This represents real progress toward the goal of synthesis, but for the time being, plants remain the food factories of the world (see Fig. 1-1).

The Basic Food-Makers

In a very real sense, the existence of plants makes animal life possible. For animals are not food-makers, and must get their foods ready made. Green plants contain *chlorophyll*, a substance which enables them to utilize the energy of sunlight in the food-making process known as *photosynthesis*. This process does not take place all at once, but is accomplished in a number of steps that represent two phases: the *light reaction* or photophase, and the *dark reaction* or synthetic phase.

The Photophase. In the light reaction, chlorophyll molecules receive light energy which is changed into and stored as chemical energy. Then the chemical energy of the chlorophyll molecule is used to split water molecules into hydrogen (H) and oxygen (O_2). The hydrogen is trapped and held by a hydrogen acceptor for further use. The oxygen becomes a by-product. Meanwhile, ADP (adenosine diphosphate) in the

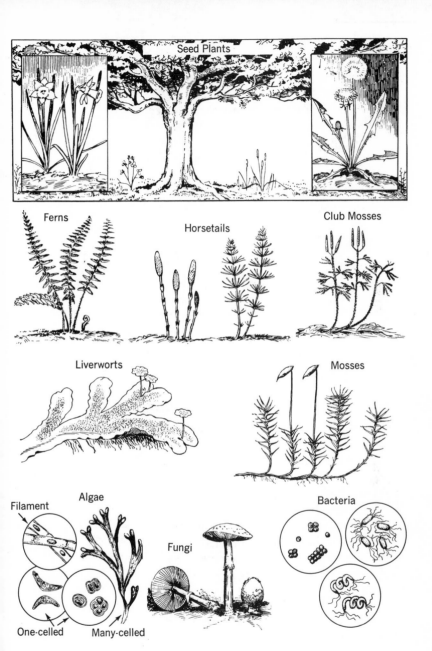

Fig. 1-1. Representatives of the major plant groups.

chloroplasts receives light energy, which is changed into chemical energy, and the ADP becomes ATP (adenosine triphosphate), and provides another source of energy for later stages in the food-making process.

The Synthetic Phase. In the dark reaction, a carbon dioxide acceptor in a chloroplast combines with carbon dioxide, and in a series of reactions which involve the trapped H (hydrogen) and the energy of ATP, a basic food substance called PGAL (phosphoglyceraldehyde) and water emerge as end products. PGAL consists of 3 carbon, 5 hydrogen, and 3 oxygen atoms ($C_3H_5O_3$) and a phosphate group, and some of it is used by the cell in its life processes. But other portions of the PGAL are now changed through a further series of reactions which involve the addition of hydrogen and the loss of phosphate groups into the familiar glucose, which has the formula $C_6H_{12}O_6$. The cell that makes glucose may discharge some of it to be used by other cells of the plant. Glucose also can be converted into sucrose or into starch.

The photo and synthetic phases of photosynthesis may be summarized as follows:

$$6\ CO_2 + 12\ H_2O + \text{light energy} \longrightarrow C_6H_{12}O_6 + 6H_2O + 6O_2$$

The reader may note that while water is a raw material and a product as well, the original 12 water molecules split into their component parts, namely the hydrogen ions (H^+) and oxygen molecules (O_2). Oxygen is liberated as a product of the reaction, as seen in the equation above. The hydrogen ions are used as has been previously described; that is, to form PGAL and, later, glucose. The oxygen in the glucose does not come from water, but from the original carbon dioxide. Thus we see that the original water molecules play an active part in the chemical reaction, and six new water molecules are liberated as an end product.

Glucose, like PGAL, may be regarded as a basic food, and there are other ways in which basic food may be produced in nature. For instance, some of the purple sulfur *bacteria* which contain chlorophyll use carbon dioxide and hydrogen sulfide (H_2S) in a process that can be described as follows:

$CO_2 + H_2S +$ light energy $\longrightarrow$ carbohydrates $+ S_2$ or H_2SO_4

The big difference in this case is that hydrogen sulfide (rather than water) is a raw material, and that sulfur (S_2) or sulfuric acid (H_2SO_4) (rather than water and oxygen) are by-products.

Chemosynthesis. In a third type of food-making known as *chemosynthesis,* the bacteria which are the food-makers *do not* contain chlorophyll. They obtain energy by combining various inorganic elements with oxygen. Then they use the energy to produce a series of reactions in which the raw materials carbon dioxide and water give rise to basic food and the by-product oxygen. This may be summarized in the following manner:

(1) inorganic element $+ O_2 \longrightarrow$ energy $+$ inorganic by-products

(2) $H_2O + CO_2 +$ energy $\longrightarrow$ basic food $+ O_2$

Food for the World

Some of the green plants we have mentioned live out on the land and others dwell in the waters of the earth, but usually fairly close to the surface where they are in contact with the all-important sunlight. The purple sulfur bacteria and the chemosynthetic bacteria are inhabitants of swamps and marshy areas. These plants are the only organisms that can make food out of inorganic substances. All other organisms are directly or indirectly dependent upon them for their sustenance.

The food-makers are eaten by a variety of animals, and these animals, in turn, are eaten by other animals. Thus in a fresh-water pond, a green plant lives and dies. Its tissues become food for various bacteria of decay, which are bacteria that feed upon dead plant or animal tissues. The bacteria prosper and become numerous. They are food, in turn, for certain single-celled animals such as the familiar *Paramecium.* These single-celled animals are eaten by tiny crustaceans, and the crustaceans may be devoured by small fish. Here we have a *food chain* in operation, which may lead from an obscure water plant to our own table. There are many of these food chains in fresh water, in the sea, and out on the land. They are complex and may branch off in various directions. Thus in the example cited, the tiny crustaceans may be eaten by insect larvae, the larvae by minnows, and the minnows by herons or other aquatic birds.

Through food chains, the carbohydrates, fats, and proteins are passed along from one organism to another. In any natural community, these organisms can be arbitrarily divided into a number of food groups, as follows:

1. The *food-makers*, which are those types that carry on photosynthesis or chemosynthesis, and include our crop plants.
2. The *herbivores*, which are the animals that feed largely on plants, such as cattle, goats, and sheep.
3. The *carnivores*, which are the animals that feed largely upon other animals, such as lions, tigers, and wildcats.
4. The *omnivores*, which are the animals that eat both plant and animal material, such as man.
5. The *parasites*, which live at the expense of plant or animal *hosts*, such as the microbes and parasitic worms.
6. The *saprophytes*, which feed upon dead plant or animal tissues, such as the bacteria of decay.

Representatives of all the food groups find their niche in a community. The big ones eat the little ones, and the little ones sometimes return the compliment. Necessarily, the lives of many plants and animals are closely interrelated. The herbivore must have plant material as food, and the saprophyte cannot prosper without a supply of dead tissues to feed upon. In the middle of everything is that restless omnivore we call man, who generally prefers variety in his diet.

In a given season, the food-makers of a community produce just so much basic food, depending upon the degree to which the physical environment is favorable. As this basic food is passed along through food chains, some of it is used up at each stage, for each animal converts some basic food to energy in order to live. From the standpoint of human food supplies we might argue that this is not economic; but on the other hand, a human diet of dried hay would not be very tempting and would be sorely lacking in protein and other nutrients. Therefore we generally prefer to let the grazing animals eat the hay, and obtain a meat supply from them later on. Nevertheless, in areas of dense human population the demand for food is so great that very little grain or any other usable plant material is fed to stock animals.

Change and Decay. Strangely enough, decay is closely related to plant production, and without this process our world would be a strange place indeed. Doubtless it would be littered with the remains of various plants and animals, and certainly the fertility of soils and waters would be greatly reduced. As it is, an occasional mammoth is found in an ice deposit where it has been more or less preserved for thousands of years.

The reader probably is aware that in addition to carbohydrates, green plants synthesize plant oils and proteins. Since animals must have all three of these general groups of food compounds—carbohydrates, fats, and proteins—their dependence upon plants is absolute.

But some of the plants are not food-makers. They are nongreen types which have no photosynthetic or chemosynthetic abilities. Most of these plants are either parasites or saprophytes. Some of them are the single-celled bacteria, and some others are known as true *fungi* (see p. 27). There are many ways in which bacteria and fungi are related to human affairs. For instance, some of them are concerned in the common processes of decay.

A tree trunk rotting away on the forest floor illustrates the nature of decay. This tree trunk once contained many living cells, which in turn were filled with carbohydrates, plant oils, and proteins. But the saprophytes have already been at work. The wood is literally alive with bacteria and fungi which depend upon its disintegrating tissues for their sustenance. Generations of these simple plants have fed upon the tree trunk, and their descendants are continuing the practice. Meanwhile, termites and ants probably are tunneling in the woody tissues, and before long, what is left of the tree will be returned to the soil.

Part of the story of the decaying tree is also the story of the *nitrogen cycle* (Fig. 1-2). This cycle is concerned with the formation and breakdown of the protein compounds which form such an important part of any living substance. We can start with the fact that a protein contains the elements carbon, hydrogen, and oxygen, and in addition, nitrogen. What happens to the nitrogen is the important factor in the nitrogen cycle.

Since green plants cannot use nitrogen in its free form, they must use nitrogen compounds known as *nitrates* in their process of manufacturing proteins. Fortunately, there are some very small organisms that can "fix" free nitrogen of the air to produce nitrates. They include the nitrogen-fixing bacteria found in soil and water, as well as some other bacteria that have this useful capacity. They also include certain *algae,* which are simple, aquatic plants. And finally, nitrates that are formed when lightning flashes across the sky fall to the earth with rains.

It may therefore be seen that natural means of nitrogen fixation exist both on land and in bodies of water. Nitrates that are produced are absorbed by green plants and used in building proteins. When plant or animal bodies die and decay, the proteins in them break down to form ammonia. Certain bacteria change some of the ammonia into nitrites and then into nitrates, and the latter can, of course, be used by the green plants again. Some other bacteria, however, break down ammonia so that free nitrogen appears again. Thus there is a natural cycle, in which the same molecule of nitrogen may at one time be in the air, and at other times be a part of an ammonia, nitrite, or nitrate compound, or a part of a protein compound in a plant or animal.

The importance of the nitrogen cycle can hardly be exaggerated. The production of plants, and therefore animals, both on land and in the water, depends very largely upon the presence of the nitrates that are essential if proteins are to be synthesized. In the nitrogen cycle, a steady flow of nitrates is made available for this process.

Before we leave this subject of bacteria and fungi, let us note that some fungi known as *molds* and some bacteria have recently assumed new importance in our affairs because they are the sources of antibiotics employed as chemical defenses against germs. In addition, some other members of this group are factors in industrial processes leading to the production of useful chemicals. This subject is discussed more extensively in Chapter 4.

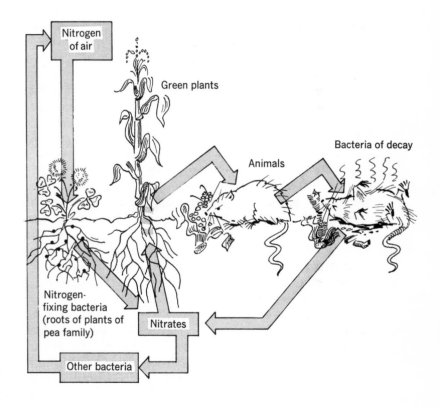

Fig. 1-2. This is a diagram to show the main features of the nitrogen cycle. Nitrogen-fixing bacteria form colonies on the roots of plants belonging to the legume family, which includes the peas and beans.

Simple Algae and Human Benefits

We have outlined two or three ways in which mankind benefits from the presence of various simple plants. These benefits are indirect, but they are of vast consequence in human economy; in fact, life as we know it would be impossible without them. First, many of the small and simple plants are among the world's basic food-makers, and their products are passed along through food chains for our ultimate benefit. Second, certain simple plants, including bacteria and fungi, are active in the processes of decay, which return various decay products to the soils and waters to be used again by subsequent generations of living things. And finally, decay is one phase of the nitrogen cycle, in which the activities of certain simple plants make available a continuing supply of nitrates for the synthesis of proteins.

What, then, are these simple plants? If the reader looks at page 27 he will find listed there five groups of algae, one group of bacteria, and one group of true fungi. This is not the complete roll call, because some groups have been omitted from the list. The groups shown are those that contain many species of direct or indirect importance to man. Among them, and especially in the case of the bacteria and true fungi, are various species that we would like to consign to limbo because they are notorious producers of disease. On the other hand, there are many other types that are useful and in some cases essential to our well-being.

Let us return to these useful types and consider a number of examples. Along the shores of the seas a variety of algae abound, along with numerous small forms of animal life. These algae and their small animal associates provide food for the larger marine animals which are of special interest to us.

Coastal waters are not the only spawning grounds of aquatic life. There are so-called "pastures of the sea," just as there are meadows on land surfaces. Far from any coast line there are many small, floating types of plants and animals that mingle at or near the sea surface, even in the colder waters. Prominent among them are the little algae known as *diatoms* (Fig. 1-3). Diatoms, along with other small floating organisms, make up what is called *plankton,* which provides a ready food supply for many of the larger marine species. Here then, wherever plankton abounds, are pastures of the sea. The existence of this plankton is vital to any projected scheme of ocean agriculture.

It may be of interest to note that in the sea the plankton "pasture" is quite different from a pasture on the land. On land, the higher plants cover most of the soil surface and provide the bulk of the basic food. In the sea, the situation is reversed, and the small, simple algae are the dominant food-makers. The diatoms, for instance, make up in numbers what

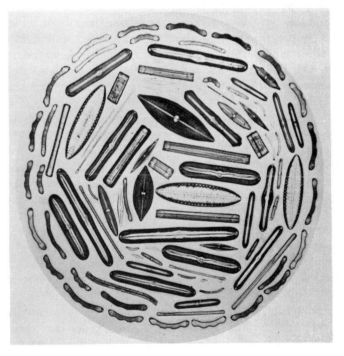

Smithsonian Institution

Fig. 1-3. A group of fresh-water diatoms. Notice the many different shapes of these little food-makers.

they lack in size, and have been called the "grasses of the sea."

Plankton, including diatoms, is also found in fresh-water ponds, lakes, and streams. Here it stands in much the same relationship to higher forms of life as it does in the sea.

We have even found direct uses for plankton. On a small scale, people in different parts of the world have strained plankton out of sea water and used it as food. In view of the fact that many plankton organisms are small animals, it is not surprising that the plankton mass has a protein content of about 50 per cent, which scarcely would be the case if the organisms were plants alone. However, because they are food-makers, plants are the key members of the plankton world.

Let us consider some of the red and brown algae described on page 27. Most algae in these groups are sea dwellers. The red algae are generally moderate in size, building up bodies that contain many cells, but with little cell specialization. The brown algae are similar as far as cell specialization goes, but some of them are much larger. The giant kelps, for instance, may develop growths 200 feet in length. Such many-celled algae or seaweeds are potential sources of food substances including vitamins and useful minerals, and they have not been overlooked in man's quest for nutrients.

Along the coasts of Asia and islands of the Pacific Ocean, the practice of eating algae, which might aptly be called "marine vegetables," was established centuries ago. The Orientals still consume quantities of the edible kelps, of which the most important belong to the genus *Laminaria*. They also favor the so-called *lavers* of the genus *Porphyra*. In fact, the Japanese have been cultivating red algae for a long time, which indicates that such foods have been in considerable demand and that ocean agriculture is more than a theoretical possibility.

Europeans and Americans have shown much less disposition to eat the algae found along their own sea coasts, but have not abstained entirely. For in the western world the food known as laver or slake is red algae of the genus *Porphyra*, and dulse or sea kale is algae of the genus *Rhodymenia*. Although these algae are not particularly good sources of nutrients, except for vitamins and minerals, they do provide flavors that some people enjoy, and fill otherwise empty stomachs.

While we may have no craving for laver or dulse, probably we have eaten algal products while not being aware of the fact. Such commodities as chocolate milk, sherbets, ice creams, puddings, and jellies may contain these products in various forms.

One alga commonly known as Irish moss (*Chondrus crispus*) has been collected along the coasts of New England and the English Islands, and used to supply bulk or "body" in blanc mange, jellies, and puddings, as well as in the production of soft drinks and beers. However, because various other substances that will serve the purpose have become available, it is no longer employed to a great extent.

Among the substitutes for Irish moss is *agar*, which is derived from some 40 different kinds of red algae that are found along various sea costs, and are mostly members of the genus *Gelidium*. Long ago, the Japanese discovered a method of extracting agar from such algae by a freezing and thawing process. In due course, they were exporting the product, which contains the carbohydrate gelose that we do not digest. The Japanese even began to raise *Gelidium* in order to provide larger supplies of the agar, which was proving useful in a number of ways. For example, agar can be added to puddings, jellies, sherbets, and ice creams. In Japan, it is mixed with various foods such as the rice dishes, and also serves as a thickener in soups. It enjoys world-wide popularity in biological laboratories as a culture medium upon which bacteria and molds may be grown. It has also been employed in making film emulsions, wrapping paper, insect sprays, silk fabrics, and cosmetics. It has utility in some tanning processes and in the preservation and canning of fish and meat. Since it absorbs water and provides non-irritating bulk in foods, it has served as a mild laxative, and as a bulk-provider in reducing diets.

We once imported large amounts of agar from Japan, but since World War II we have obtained some of our supply from American sources. Other countries in which agar has been or is being produced include Australia, China, the East Indies, Mexico, and the Soviet Union.

The large kelps have a further value in some parts of the world. They are burned, and the resulting ash becomes a source of iodine, potash, and soda. Moreover, kelps are used as animal food in some lands, and also in compounding certain types of fertilizers that have a vogue in Europe and the Orient. Finally, kelps and sargassums are prized by the Orientals as sources of some of their medicines.

Before leaving the subject of algae, we may note a few more things about the little, single-celled diatoms. We have indicated that they are basic food-makers and important factors in plankton. But they possess two other characteristics that we should not overlook. One is that each cell is enclosed in two valves that are composed of silica. The other is that diatoms store reserve foods in the form of plant oils.

In past geologic times, diatoms clearly have engaged in veritable population explosions. When this happens, the silicious "shells" of dead diatoms pile up on the sea bottom, where their presence results in the formation of *diatomaceous earth*. Some California deposits of this material are hundreds of feet in thickness. Diatomaceous earth is used in manufacturing abrasives, some soaps, and various filters. In addition, diatoms may well have had something to do with the origin of certain oil deposits, either as basic food-makers or as direct contributors to the oil pool.

At the present time, some of the simple, single-celled algae are attracting special attention. Among them is *Chlorella*, which has been used in a number of experiments designed to reveal the process by which green plants make foods. *Chlorella* also merits special study because, when compared with other plants, it has a relatively high protein content. This seems important at a time when populations are on the increase and when we are giving serious thought to space exploration, for *Chlorella* cultures can be raised without too much difficulty. It would, of course, take many of these tiny plants to make a food article as large as a cracker, but if it were necessary, they probably could be produced in numbers that stagger the imagination. Of course, in order for us to do this we would need sunlight, minerals, water, and the necessary knowhow.

Plant Partnerships

Some of the simple, non-green plants manage to survive by living in *symbiotic relationships*. A good example is furnished by the lichens we see growing on rocks and tree trunks in places that are reasonably moist at least part of the time. A lichen consists of two plants—an alga and a fungus. The alga contains chlorophyll and makes the food for both plants. The fungus aids in the partnership by holding fast to the surface on which the lichen is growing and by absorbing moisture when it is available. Both plants are believed to profit by the association, thus meeting the requirements of a symbiotic relationship.

Even lichens are known to affect our food economy. In cold and barren countries, they often are a conspicuous part of the plant life, and serve as food for browsing animals such as reindeer and caribou. Their presence on rock surfaces causes a slow disintegration of the rock material, and thus contributes to soil formation. Reasonably hungry people have even been known to eat lichens when nothing more substantial was available.

We also obtain some commercial products from certain lichens. Several types are the sources of cudbear or archil, a blue or red dye used to color bitters, fabrics, and drugs. The litmus that is often used as a chemical indicator may also be derived from lichens. The substance known as oak moss, which is employed extensively in making perfumes and scented soaps, represents various European species of lichens.

Fungi as Foods

The fungi that we eat—or at least eat deliberately—are members of the true fungus group (see page 27), and are generally known as *mushrooms*. There are several thousand different types of mushrooms, some of them edible and others definitely poisonous. Certain edible puffballs and morels are fairly well marked, and can be recognized by the expert with reasonable certainty. But there are various poisonous mushrooms that look much like the edible ones, and it is in this fact that danger abides; the expert *must really be expert* if wild mushrooms are to be collected and consumed with any degree of security. Amateurs and people with experimental urges will live longer if they purchase their mushrooms in the market.

The practice of eating mushrooms is, however, deep-seated and world wide. It probably dates back to the all but forgotten times when men were largely food gatherers. The Europeans and Asiatics have eaten wild mushrooms for centuries, in defiance of the fact that some of their less cautious associates have now and again been poisoned fatally.

From the standpoint of nourishment, mushrooms do not compare favorably with many other foods, for they consist of over 90 per cent water; but they do contain useful proteins, minerals, and vitamins. Moreover, many mushroom eaters are not really on the lookout for high energy foods, except perhaps, to avoid them. And mushrooms add a great deal to the attractiveness of many food combinations.

The type of mushroom raised for the market in the United States is *Agaricus campestris,* which had its advent on these shores near the close of the past century. Annual production now runs over 100 million pounds, despite the fact that the cultivated crop cannot be raised out of doors. Most of it is grown in abandoned mines, old quarries, caves, and special buildings; prepared and planted "trays" are now available for purchase, and some home owners have taken to raising their own mushrooms in basements. In any case, the temperature, humidity, and ventilation must be carefully controlled.

A mushroom of this type consists of an underground structure called a "spawn," which is really a *mycelium:* filaments which obtain food from decaying matter in the soil. The part above ground consists of a stem and a cap. On the underside of the cap are the gills, and here reproductory cells called spores are discharged. Experts use these spores to develop *pure culture spawn,* which is sold to mushroom raisers.

The next step is to prepare suitable beds or trays in which the spawn may be planted. Such beds must naturally contain the decaying organic matter from which the myceliums of the mushrooms can obtain nourishment. This material is called *compost.* One system is to use horse manure to which gypsum and perhaps some cottonseed meal or brewer's grain has been added. Another system employs a mixture of hay, corn cobs, gypsum, and commercial fertilizer. In either case, the compost must be pasteurized by heating so that undesirable fungi, insects, and worms will not appear in it.

The pasteurized compost, in beds or trays, is now ready for use. Spawn is scattered over the surface of the beds and allowed to grow for two or three weeks at temperatures between 65° F and 70° F. In due course, the desired mushrooms begin to push up out of the soil, and continue to do so for two months or more. During this period, the humidity must be held at a rather high level to prevent the edible caps from drying.

European mushroom growers also depend upon *Agaricus campestris,* but in Japan the story is quite different. Here the species *Cortinellus edodes* is raised on logs. Most of the cultivated mushrooms are eaten fresh or are canned in this country, but the Japanese type is more generally dried, and thus kept in readiness for inclusion in a number of soups.

The delight of some gourmets, known as the truffle, is also a fungus. An English species, *Tuber aestivum,* has a mycelium which grows in symbiotic relationship with the roots of beech trees. A French and Mediterranean type, *Tuber melanosporum,* develops its mycelium in symbiotic relationship with the roots of oak trees. Apparently this is most likely to happen when the soil overlies limestone deposits. The edible portion of these fungi is a warty, bluish-black fruiting body about two or three inches in diameter, which is produced underground, sometimes a foot below the surface.

Truffles were known to both the ancient Greeks and the

Romans, and presumably have been collected and eaten in Europe for 20 centuries or more. Since the fruiting bodies develop underground, finding the plants is something of a problem. However, the soil above the fruiting bodies tends to crack a little bit, and certain flies are attracted to the spot, possibly by the odor of the fungi. Also, trained dogs have been used to locate spots where truffles lie buried. In the Mediterranean area, truffle pigs perform a similar service in determining appropriate places to dig. A well-trained truffle pig is no ordinary porker, but a valuable animal in the same class as a good canine retriever.

It is well known, of course, that certain fungi have an important role in the production of some kinds of cheeses, such as blue cheese, gorgonzola, and roquefort. Spores of the mold *Penicillium roqueforti* are introduced into the newly formed cheese, which is then aged so that the molds will have time to develop and add the spots of greenish color and the flavor characteristic of the product. The mold *Penicillium camemberti* stands in somewhat similar relationship to camembert cheese.

Plant Species and Plant Groups

In concluding our overview of plants in general and simple plants in particular, it may be of interest to see how the simple types relate to and differ from their more complex relatives. Our point of departure may well be the manner in which plants are named.

Scientists refer to the particular *kind* of plant as the *species.* This does not mean that all members of the species are *exactly alike,* for in nature it is recognized that individual variation is the rule rather than the exception. But it does mean that the members of the species are sufficiently alike that some expert has decided that they can be grouped together.

Generally, a well-known species has more than one common name, a fact which is likely to cause confusion. A remedy has been provided by giving all plants Latin (or latinized) names. Thus although the American elm is also known as the water elm or the white elm, if we refer to it as *Ulmus americana,* confusion cannot result.

There are larger classification groups than the species. Two or more related species, for instance, make up a *genus.* For example, the American elm is *Ulmus americana,* and the slippery elm is *Ulmus fulva.* Both belong to the genus *Ulmus,* and this name is written first. In each case, the second name is the name of the particular species.

Similarly, two or more related genera may be grouped together to form a *family.* There is more individual variation in a family than in a genus or a species. Still, the members of a family will all have many similar characteristics.

In much the same way, two or more related families make up an *order,* two or more related orders make up a *class,* and two or more related classes make up a *phylum.* As a rule, a phylum is a large group, and while all of its members will still have one or more common characteristics, they may be expected to exhibit quite a few differences as well.

The Plant Kingdom includes a number of phyla. For reference purposes, a table of these large groups and some of their subdivisions is included on the following pages. The reader is cautioned, however, that some of the phyla and sub-groups have been omitted from the table, which is limited to plants that have the greatest direct or indirect utility in human affairs.

Selected List of Plant Groups

Phylum Tracheophyta.

The "Higher" Plants. Develop vascular tissues. Include angiosperms and gymnosperms—the so-called seed plants.

Class Angiospermae.

Angiosperms. So-called "flowering plants," but other plants also develop flower structures. Angiosperm seeds are enclosed in seed cases. About 200,000 species.

Subclass Diocotyledoneae.

Dicot Plants. Bear two cotyledons or seed leaves. This group includes composite, parsley, dogwood, birch, oak, walnut, maple, cactus, bean, rose, mint, snapdragon, phlox, olive, heather, buckwheat, poppy, mustard, elm, mallow, magnolia, laurel and other families.

Subclass Monocotyledoneae.

Monocot Plants. Have single seed leaves. This group includes orchid, iris, amaryllis, sedge, grass, palm, lily, pondweed, water plaintain and other families.

Class Gymnospermae.

Gymnosperms. Evergreen trees and shrubs which produce cones. Seeds not enclosed in seed cases. About 600 species, which are mostly conifers such as pines, hemlocks, and firs. The gingko tree and the cycads also belong in this class.

Class Lycopodineae.

Club Mosses. Creeping stems give rise to upright stems that bear cones; small leaves that are arranged spirally. About 600 modern species.

Class Equisetineae.

Horsetails. An underground stem gives rise to upright, jointed stems with scale-like leaves. About 25 modern species.

Class Filicineae.

Ferns. Adult plant has an underground stem from which leaves or fronds develop. About 10,000 modern species.

Phylum Bryophyta.

Small non-vascular plants. Characteristically food-makers. A gametophyte generation is dominant over a sporophyte generation, which is the reverse of the situation among the higher plants. About 25,000 species.

Class Musci.

Mosses. These are the more common and well-known members of this phylum.

Class Hepaticae.

Liverworts. In these plants, the gametophyte grows as a flattened thallus.

Phylum Eumycophyta.

True Fungi. Parasites, saprophytes, or live in symbiotic associations. No chlorophyll. Included are puffballs, mushrooms, rust and smut fungi, mildews, yeasts, and molds. About 90,000 known species.

Phylum Schizomycophyta.

Bacteria. Single-celled forms without organized nuclei and usually without chlorophyll. About 2500 described species, which include parasites and saprophytes.

Phylum Rhodophyta.

Red Algae. Food-making plants, but their chlorophyll is generally masked by red pigments. Most of them are found in the sea. About 2500 species.

Phylum Phaeophyta.

Brown Algae. Food-makers whose chlorophyll is generally masked by brown pigments. Include the rockweeds, kelps, and sargassums. About 1000 species that are mostly found in the sea.

Phylum Chrysophyta.

Yellow-green Algae, Golden-brown Algae, and Diatoms. Food-makers. Foods are stored as plant oils. About 6000 species. Represented in both fresh and salt water.

Phylum Chlorophyta.

Green Algae. Food-makers. Pigments are in plastids. Found in fresh and salt water. About 5000 species.

Phylum Cyanophyta.

Blue-green Algae. Food-makers. Contain blue pigments in addition to the green chlorophyll. Pigment granules are not organized in plastids, and normal nuclei are absent. Found in fresh and salt water. About 2500 species.

2

Cereals, Vegetables, and Condiments

Man probably has attempted to eat almost everything of plant or animal origin at one time or another. Primitive European tribes of the middle stone age devoured impressive numbers of wild horses and other larger animals, and at the same time, they probably knew about the food uses of a good many plants. In fact, during the late stone age it is clear that they were raising some of the staple food plants, and from ancient tombs along the Nile River come evidences that grains were being produced at the same or an even earlier period in this area. It may be suspected that some peoples were cultivating plants 150 centuries ago, but about 100 centuries appears to be a more probable date. Perhaps the first types raised were root crops such as yams and taro, because in areas where the climate permitted, such species might have been easier to deal with than the seed crops that gave rise to the modern grains.

Since this early use and cultivation of plants took place long before historical records were kept, it is not surprising that the origins of some modern favorites are subject to dispute. In some cases, their wild ancestors appear to have vanished from the face of the earth. In others, the mystery may relate to an origin that goes back to more than one ancestor. And of course nomadic tribes may have carried some plants far from the scene of their nativity. Although fragments of the story of early cultivation are added as new "finds" are made, we probably shall never have a full account.

But it is accepted that the cultivation of plants was closely linked with early civilizations in at least four areas: the Mediterranean area, including North Africa and southern Europe; the central and west Asian area, including the so-called Fertile Crescent which extended from ancient Palestine

28

to Babylonia along the northern rim of the Arabian Desert, as well as lands farther to the north and east; the southeast Asian area; and the tropical American area. Between the first two areas there was more or less communication at an early date. Wheat, for example, was an ancient food in both the west Asian and Mediterranean areas. It may, in fact, have had a multiple origin. Indian corn, or maize, on the other hand, was developed in the tropical American area, and presumably was unknown to inhabitants of the old world until the voyages of discovery.

Apparently the ancients did a good job of assessing the potential usefulness of the many land plants they encountered. From thousands of species, they chose a limited number that they elected to raise. Obviously they were seeking desirable seeds in some cases, and fruits, leaves, stems, or roots in others. During the past 20 centuries, we have not added materially to the variety of plants that we cultivate; rather, we have concentrated upon improving the types that were passed along to us by our ancestors, and establishing some of the more adaptive species in areas where formerly they did not exist.

The bulk of the plant foods used by man now come from cultivated sources. But human progress has not been equal for all peoples, and there are various natives, especially in the tropics and subtropics, who still depend to a considerable extent upon the "wild" plant foods. Even in long settled areas with relatively advanced cultures, the native plants of field and forest provide a certain amount of sustenance.

Some of our economic plants are *annuals*, which means that they sprout, grow, produce seeds, and die within a single season. Others are *biennials*, which require two years to complete their life cycles. And some, such as the forest trees, are *perennial* plants, which live on through more than two seasons; in fact for centuries in some cases.

Forage and Cereals

Forage Crops. If we were to select the plant group that has been of greatest food use to man, our choice would have to be the grass family. From it men have derived the cereal grains that are so important in modern world economy. But there also are hundreds of grass species that have never been cultivated. When the early settlers moved into the interior of our country, they found the vast prairies of the central states stretching before them, and somewhat later they encountered the short grass areas of the great plains. Originally, these grasses were all native, and they provided food for cattle, horses, and other domesticated animals.

Later on, of course, the native grasses were replaced to a greater or lesser extent by cultivated species from the old world which provided better crops of hay for the feeding of livestock, and by such plants as the clovers and alfalfas, which are not grasses. The combination of grasses, clovers, alfalfas, and some other plants that animals browse upon make up what we call *forage crops*.

Timothy hay (*Phleum pratense*) is perhaps the favorite forage plant in the United States. But there are others, including the *sorghums* of the genus *Holcus,* such as kafir corn, milo maize, and durra. These sorghums are grass plants that have been cultivated for a very long time in Africa and Southeast Asia, both for their seeds and as forage. In a recent year, nearly 500 million bushels of sorghum grain were produced in this country, largely destined to become animal food. Use of the sorghums as crop plants, both here and abroad, depends upon the fact that they will grow in dryland areas, such as our great plains.

In much of the great plains area, however, there has been a disposition to use the natural growths of grasses. In fact, attempts to plow and plant the drylands have often led to dust storms, dust bowls, and economic disaster. Other nations also have their grazing lands, as represented by the steppes of the Soviet Union and the pampas of Argentina. Lands used in this fashion often are potentially fertile, but without irrigation they are not suited to many types of crop production. But a mixture of grasses and other plants that serve as forage will grow on them, and we depend upon cattle and sheep to convert this food material into beef and mutton.

Wheat. One of the first grass plants to be brought under cultivation was wheat, of which there are several species and a great many varieties belonging to the genus *Triticum*. Most of them are annual plants, but the group does include a few perennials. The cultivation of wheat can be traced back at least 6000 years. Just where and how it became such an important factor in human affairs, however, remains something of a puzzle. Perhaps it was first raised somewhere along the Fertile Crescent where the rim of the desert encroached upon the highlands. But you can also make a case for the origin of wheat farther east in Asia, or in the Mediterranean area. It has been proposed that the cultivated wheats had more than one ancestor, and came from two or all three of these areas.

But in any event, wheat is an old world plant, which the Spaniards first brought to Middle America early in the sixteenth century. Today, it is raised extensively on all of the world's continents, for the simple reason that there are so many varieties of wheat adapted to different conditions of life. Thus there are winter wheats that are planted in the fall and spring wheats that are planted in the spring; there are wheats that will mature in a short growing season; wheats that are resistant to certain diseases; wheats that will grow upon poor soil and dry soil; wheats that have hard grains; and wheats that have soft grains. Moreover, there are wheats that are good for producing bread flour, others that are reserved for spaghetti and macaroni, and wheats that have stems used in fabricating carpets, baskets, and hats. We eat many foods that are made wholly or in part from wheat flour, we feed vast amounts of wheat products to livestock, and we use this grain in the manufacture of starch, breakfast foods, alcohol, and other products.

Raising wheat is largely a matter of preparing the soil, sowing the seed, and then sitting back to wait for the harvest (Fig. 2-1). This does not mean, however, that a good harvest is always forthcoming. Favorable or unfavorable weather is a factor that must be reckoned with, and wheat crops can be badly damaged by insects, and diseases caused by rusts, smuts, and viruses.

International Harvester
Fig. 2-1.   Combine harvesting of wheat in the American west.

Nevertheless, we can raise some kinds of wheat where a good many other crops probably will fail, and wheat is high in food value and can be stored for a long time under proper conditions. Such being the case, it is small wonder that wheat has become the world's favorite among the cereal grains.

Indian Corn or Maize.   Another grass plant of great importance is Indian corn (*Zea mays*), which is also known as *maize*. When we talk about "corn" in the United States, everyone knows that we mean Indian corn, but in some other parts of the world "corn" means any of the cereal grains. Early European explorers who came to North, Central, and South America found a number of varieties of Indian corn being raised in all of these areas. This suggested that the practice was by no means new, because it takes time to develop different varieties when we must depend upon the age-old practice of mass selection.

The ancient kingdoms of the Incas, Mayans, and Aztecs had developed a food economy that centered around Indian corn. Early inhabitants of our Southwest and some of the mound builders who preceded the Indians of pioneer days had carried corn as far north as Canada. Some ears and grains of corn from remote times have been preserved in out of the way places such as caves. Radioactive carbon dating indicated that the oldest of these finds goes back to about 2000 B.C. But there is lingering suspicion that Indian corn was raised somewhere in the Americas at a still earlier date. Modern types include pod corn, which has little commercial value, popcorn, flint corn, soft corn, dent corn, sweet corn, and waxy corn.

The origin of *Zea mays* presents another intriguing mystery. No wild species of the genus *Zea* are known to exist at the present time. Where did the cultivated type with its numerous varieties come from? One former theory held that it developed from the grass plant teosinte in Mexico or Central America, but there are serious objections to this idea. A more probable theory is that it came from a wild pod corn somewhere in the Americas. To date, no such pod corn has been found, but of course it is possible that the wild ancestor perished along the way. It is also possible that, through *hybridization*, that is, the crossing of two different varieties to combine the desirable traits of each variety, more than one grass plant contributed to the origin of Indian corn. There has even been some suspicion that corn may have been brought from Asia by early migrants who crossed over from Siberia to Alaska, and then drifted southward in the course of several generations.

But whatever its antecedents may have been, there are rather clear indications that early cultivated corn was a popcorn, and also a pod corn, the latter being a type in which small husks develop around each of the kernels.

After Europeans reached the new world, Indian corn was carried to the other continents, and it is now raised in portions of Europe, Asia, and Africa where the climate is favorable. In our own country, corn is clearly the "king" among grains, and in recent years production has varied from about 3 billion to almost 4 billion bushels. This compares with an annual production of about 1¼ billion bushels of wheat. Relatively more of the corn, however, goes into livestock foods. In a recent year, for example, the average United States citizen consumed about 28 pounds of corn products, and at the same time, about 118 pounds of wheat flour. Clearly, most of the corn crop was either stored or used to fatten cattle and pigs.

In modern times, the development of hybrid corn seed has resulted in a new industry of seed production, and has also given rise to substantially increased yields. Farmers are sometimes a bit reluctant to try out new crops, but the benefits accruing from the use of hybrid corn seed apparently were too obvious to be resisted.

The corn products that we consume directly include breakfast foods, popcorn, canned sweet corn, corn on the cob, cornmeal, corn oil, corn sugar, corn liquors, corn syrup, and hominy. But it should not be thought that the utility of this versatile plant is limited to the grain it bears. Grain, stalks, and husks are involved in the production of many things, including adhesives, artificial fibers, charcoal, cornstarch, elastomers, explosives, fuels, nutrient solutions for growing molds, packaging materials, paper, pasteboard, plastics, industrial alcohol, solvents, silage, and sizing for manufacturing processes.

Wild Oats and "Tame" Oats.   Oats rank third among the cereal grains produced in the United States; in a recent year, the domestic yield amounted to over a billion bushels, only slightly behind that of wheat. There are several species of cultivated oats belonging to the genus *Avena,* and the most popular one is *Avena sativa.* Several wild species of the same genus still appear in nature, and the cultivated types have a marked tendency to "escape." It seems quite possible that more than one wild ancestor gave rise to the oats we raise, and these ancestors may have come from the Mediterranean area, the central and west Asian area, or the southeast Asian area. Cultivation evidently was begun a long time ago, but perhaps does not go back as far as the practice of raising wheat and some other grains.

Northern Europe, northern Asia, the United States, and

Canada are all major oat-producing areas, and the plant is also grown in parts of North Africa, Australia, and South America. Oats are relatively hardy, and will survive where the climate is too cold for many other crops. Also, like some wheats, oats prosper on fairly poor soils. The one essential factor for growth is a good supply of soil moisture. Oat plants may be raised and harvested in a manner similar to wheat, or they may be grown with other plants, and even as a part of forage crops.

In America, about three-fourths of the oat crop is used to feed domesticated animals. Actually, oats have quite respectable food value; nevertheless, in a recent year, the average United States citizen consumed only about 3½ pounds of oat products, including oatmeal and rolled oats.

The Rice Plants. Cultivation of rice was begun a very long time ago, presumably in the southeast Asian area, where some marsh grass gave rise to *Oryza sativa*. Today, there are thousands of rice varieties, most of them adapted to growth on marshy or flooded lands, but including some upland types that will produce crops if enough rain falls. Rice plants yield a useful straw, but their main importance rests with the fact that some form of boiled rice is a staple food for about half of the world's population. Boiled rice has a high carbohydrate content, but needs to be supplemented by proteins and fats from other sources. Polished rice, which is rice with the husks removed, is notoriously deficient in vitamins.

Early settlers began to raise rice in the United States near the end of the seventeenth century. At present, most of the domestic crop comes from coastal areas of the South, and from California. But annual production in the United States only amounts to about one-twelfth of world production, which usually approximates 6 billion bushels. Rice also is grown to some extent in southern Europe, North Africa, and South America, but the chief production center remains in the southeast Asian area, including the Philippines (Fig. 2-2).

American wild rice, *Zizania aquatica*, is a semi-aquatic grass plant, but not a true rice. It formerly grew in large quantities along the eastern mud flats and in the lake region

Fig. 2-2.   A flooded rice paddy in Thailand with rice being replanted.

of the north central states and Canada, and is still well-represented in the latter region. The grain has been collected and used by Indians for no one knows how long, and today it is packaged and sold in domestic markets. The limited supply, however, makes wild rice something of a luxury food.

Apparently there have been no serious attempts to cultivate wild rice, other than to plant it here and there for the benefit of wild ducks. This is done, however, with ulterior motives. If the ducks are lured to the rice flats during the hunting season, they are likely to find these areas populated by gunners.

Barley Plants. Barley plants are also members of the grass family, and belong to the genus *Hordeum.* The first grain that men raised may have come from these plants, for barley was known to Europeans in the late stone age. The domestic stock may have had more than one ancestor, and may have come from the Mediterranean, the central and west Asian, or the southeast Asian areas. At present, there are several species and many varieties of cultivated barley, as might be expected in the case of a plant that has been under man's dominion for so long a time.

Barley is now grown extensively in northern Europe, Asia, and North America. A recent year saw almost 400 million bushels produced in the United States, whereas in the same year, the rice and rye crops amounted to about 53 million bushels and 27 million bushels respectively. One reason why barley is favored is because it can be grown all the way from the semitropics to Canada and Alaska. To some extent it serves as a forage crop, and most of the grain produced in the new world becomes livestock food. But barley is also useful in making soups and breakfast foods, and no small amount goes into the production of alcoholic beverages. At one time, barley flour was the basis of the breads of Europe and Asia, and some of it still serves in this capacity.

Rye Plants.   Compared with barley and wheat, rye (*Secale ceareale*) is a comparative newcomer, but nevertheless, its ancestry is in some doubt, although it appears to have come from the central and west Asian areas. Even today, there are only a few cultivated varieties, although rye has been a staple crop in northern Europe and Asia for centuries.

Rye plants are noted for their hardiness. To be sure, they probably will grow best where the soil is fertile and the climate moderate, but they will also grow on relatively poor soil, where the climate is cold and on the dry side.

Today, the world's supply of rye is still largely produced in Europe and Asia, to provide flour for the making of rye bread. Even blighted rye is sometimes consumed, despite the known danger of ergotism, as described on page 101. In America, rye is far less of a favorite, but is raised extensively in some of the northern states. Part of the crop becomes animal food, and a smaller amount goes into rye bread, rye whiskey, and industrial alcohol. Rye also serves as a forage crop, and its straw is employed in various ways, including the manufacture of paper and hats.

The Millets.   Our account of the grasses in relation to food supplies would be incomplete without some reference to the millets. They are a group of plants that includes several genera such as *Panicum, Echinochloa,* and *Setaria.* Such evidences as we have indicate that some of them were raised in the southeast Asian area at a very early date, and one type provided food for Europeans during the late stone age. Like the sorghums, millets will grow in relatively dry areas. They produce edible seeds, although these seeds are small.

Millets are now grown in many parts of the world, including Asia, Europe, Africa, and North America. In our own country, production is centered in the dry, western areas, and the crop is used primarily as forage, although also as a source of the small seeds we feed to birds. Elsewhere in the world millets are also regarded as forage plants, but their seeds are often cooked and eaten.

Grass Plants, Forage, and Cereal Grains.   In summarizing our use of grass plants, it should be clear that hay plants and some of the sorghums are raised almost exclusively for forage. The cereal grains include wheat, maize, oats, rice, barley, rye, other sorghums, and the millets, and some of them also provide forage to a greater or lesser extent. But by and large, the cereal grains are cultivated for their seeds. All of the foregoing plants are members of the grass family. As the reader may readily infer, their importance in relation to human affairs is of first rank.

Buckwheat Is Not a Grass.   Before we leave the subject of forage and seed crops, we should at least mention another type, although it is neither a grass plant nor a true cereal grain. This is buckwheat, represented by two species of the genus *Fagopyrum.* It appears that buckwheat was first cultivated in central Asia, where wild relatives are still to be found, and at a time that postdates the cultivation of both wheat and barley. Although buckwheat grows better under more favorable conditions, it will yield crops on fairly poor and dry soils.

At present, buckwheat is most popular in northern Europe and Asia. Its production in the United States has declined from over 8 million bushels in 1935 to less than a million bushels in a recent year. Buckwheat seeds are sometimes used in soups, especially in the old world, but are more generally milled to yield buckwheat flour. We mix buckwheat flour with wheat flour to produce the mixture used in cooking buckwheat griddle cakes. Otherwise, the seeds go into livestock food, and the rest of the plant may serve as forage or green fertilizer.

The Legume Plants

The use of clover and alfalfa plants, which are members of the bean or legume family, has already been mentioned in discussing forage crops. But the importance of *legumes* in the food realm has many other facets. A variety of beans belonging to the genus *Phaseolus* were cultivated long ago in tropical America; the broad bean (*Vicia faba*) is an ancient type from the Mediterranean area; and the soybean (*Glycine max*) is another very old one from the southeast Asian area. In the ancient kingdoms of the Aztecs, Mayans, and Incas, beans appear to have had an importance akin to that of Indian corn. They have similar importance in some parts of the world today, and for good reasons.

As plant products go, the seeds of legumes have rather high protein content—as much as 35 per cent in the case of soybeans. This is a significant and compelling factor in any land where meat supplies are limited. Carbohydrates are well represented also in the seeds of legumes, and soybeans in particular contain a significant quantity of plant oil. Then there is the added benefit that many legumes provide good forage, and that some of them are grown and simply plowed under to increase the fertility of the soil. The latter practice relates to the fact that nitrogen-fixing bacteria colonize on the legume roots and produce nitrates that can be used by the legumes and other green plants in protein synthesis.

Beans from the Old World. The only bean available to

Europeans in pre-Columbian times was the broad bean. It has been cultivated for so long that its geographical origin is uncertain; perhaps it came out of the Fertile Crescent, and perhaps it was first raised in the Mediterranean area. Whatever the facts may be, this large bean, which has never achieved real popularity on our side of the Atlantic, has remained a favorite in Europe, where it is raised both for its seeds and as a forage crop. In the course of time, a large number of varieties have been developed.

The soybean has been cultivated in the southeast Asian area for at least 50 centuries. For some strange reason in view of its obvious usefulness, this bean did not receive acceptance in Europe and the Americas until the present century. Meanwhile, the Europeans had long since added the common bean (*Phaseolus vulgaris*), imported from tropical America, to their growing collection of food plants. Today, however, the soybean holds top rank among the legumes. It is raised successfully in both tropical and temperate areas, and in a recent year American farmers produced nearly 700 million bushels of soybean seeds.

As might be expected in a cultivated plant of such antiquity, the soybean is now represented by hundreds of varieties. In the Orient, vast quantities of this bean are used as human food, and sprouts of the plant are also eaten. Together with other ingredients it is the source of soybean sauce. In America, it is common practice to extract oil from soybeans, and this oil goes into foods and various industrial products. Soybean seeds also are sources of adhesives and plastics, and a large proportion of the United States' crop serves as animal food.

The cowpea, *Vigna sinensis,* is another old world type that is more bean-like than pea-like. Perhaps its original home was in central Africa, but on the other hand, it has been raised in the Orient for centuries. It is now grown in the warmer areas of both hemispheres, largely to produce forage and seeds that are fed to animals. The "black-eyed pea," however, is a variety of cowpea that people commonly eat.

The mung bean, *Phaseolus aureus,* is an ancient crop plant from the southeast Asian area, which is now raised to some extent in the United States. Among other things, it serves as a source of the bean sprouts that appear on the menus of Chinese restaurants.

Beans from the Americas. The common, garden, kidney, French, or haricot bean (*Phaseolus vulgaris*) was an important food plant in all of the ancient kingdoms of the American tropics. Many varieties of this species exist, some being bush beans and others pole beans or climbers. Some are raised for use as forage, some for their seeds, and in the case of snap beans or green beans, both seeds and pods are eaten. In Europe, people may refer to any of the modern varieties of this bean as "kidney beans," but in America, "kidney bean" means one variety whose seeds are dark red and kidney shaped.

Despite the fact that many other plant foods are available, over 20 million tons of dry, edible beans were produced in the United States in a recent year. In addition, imposing amounts of fresh and frozen green beans were consumed. People of other lands have also taken kindly to this American import, which has the happy faculty of surviving on a variety of soils so long as temperatures do not drop to freezing levels.

The lima bean, *Phaseolus limensis*, is believed to be a product of the ancient Inca farmers. Recent discoveries indicate that it was being raised along the coast of Peru 6000 years ago. It also is represented today by both bush and climbing varieties. A related bean, *Phaseolus lunatus*, is similar, but produces smaller seeds. Lima beans appear on the market as fresh, frozen, canned, and dried products. They have not been as widely accepted in Europe as the common garden beans.

Legumes that Grow as Trees. Not all of the legume plants grow as herbs. Mesquite shrubs and trees of the genus *Prosopis* are native to our Southwest, Mexico, Central America, and northern South America. One southwestern type bears seed pods which provide some human food, as well as food for other animals. Another species from this area is now raised in Hawaii, where its seed pods are ground to provide livestock food. African natives use the seeds of a related genus to make a type of flour.

An old world legume tree of some importance is the carob or algaroba (*Ceratonia siliqua*), which is now raised in various warm-temperate countries, including the United States. This species appears to be of Mediterranean or west Asian origin, and it produces beans in pods. Both pods and seeds have been used as human and livestock food for centuries. A meal made from the beans is sometimes mixed with wheat flour to make bread. The pods of this tree are rather remarkable because of their high sugar content.

Peanuts from South America. The peanut, *Arachis hypogaea*, is another legume plant for which the world apparently must thank the Inca farmers. It seems that peanuts were carried from South America to Africa soon after the voyages of discovery, and were then brought back to our southern states from the dark continent. Today, peanuts are raised in North and South America, and in Africa, Asia, and Europe as well. The United States crop has totaled over two billion pounds in some years.

As a matter of fact, peanuts are not really "nuts." What we call "nuts" in this case are developed in pods or fruits that form underground. Peanuts are important sources of edible oils and oils used in industry. They also go into peanut butter, peanut candies, and are roasted and salted. In this country, a good many of them are employed to fatten pigs.

Old World Peas. Peas are among the well-known legumes, and apparently were first raised in the Mediterranean area prior to the beginning of the Christian Era. Generally, they are more hardy than most beans, and do well in a fairly cool climate, provided there is enough soil moisture. Two common types are the garden pea (*Pisum sativum*) and the field pea (*Pisum arvense*).

In North America, garden peas are a popular crop in Canada and the northern states. They are raised for human food and for forage, and the seeds are eaten fresh, frozen, and canned. The so-called sugar peas are varieties of garden peas that have tender pods, and these pods can be eaten along with the seeds.

Field peas provide us with the "split peas" that are often used in soups. In a recent year, about 3½ million bags of dry field peas were produced in the United States. This species is now raised in all countries within the temperate zones. In addition to the seeds, other parts of the plant have value, being used as forage.

A "Pea" that Is Not a Pea. The chick pea, *Cicer arietinum*, is not a true pea, but it is a legume plant. It comes from the Mediterranean area, and represents one of the older cultivations. It is now raised in many lands, but has never become very popular in the United States, although there appears to be a growing tendency to use it in vegetable soups. Its relatively large seeds have good food value, but it does not qualify as a forage plant. It does, however, have the advantage of growing successfully on fairly dry soils.

The Lentil Plant. The geographical origin of the lentil plant, *Lens esculenta*, appears to be lost in antiquity. That men were raising lentils at a very early date, however, is well established. Lentils are legumes of the vetch type, and there are many modern varieties. Their seeds are relatively small, usually flattened, and variously colored. Lentil plants will grow on rather infertile and sandy soil, and will serve as forage crops as well as sources of seeds.

Somehow lentils came to be regarded as a staple food of poor people in times past, but this is not necessarily the case today. In fact, lentil soup has become a popular dish in the United States. Europe, Asia, and Africa are centers of lentil production, but the plants are also raised in North America, and packages of lentil seeds and cans of lentil soup are available in American markets.

Legumes and Forage. By this time the reader probably is aware that most of the cultivated legumes can and do serve as forage. There are some, in fact, that are primarily or exclusively forage plants. Chief among them is alfalfa, *Medicago sativa*, which is another old, cultivated plant that hails from the central Asian region. One of the activities of the Medes and Persians in ancient times was growing alfalfa. A number of varieties have been developed, and alfalfa has become an important plant in many parts of the world, including our own country.

Alfalfa is a perennial, which sends its tap root as much as 50 feet down into the ground. No doubt this explains why this excellent forage plant can withstand droughts that would spell doom to many crops. It also tolerates both hot and cold weather.

Other important forage legumes include vetches of the genus *Vicia* and various species of clover belonging to the genera *Trifolium* and *Melilotus*. The clovers include types that are annuals, biennials, and perennials. Possibly they were first cultivated in Europe, in much more recent times than alfalfa.

In a somewhat different category are two legumes from the southeast Asian area, which are used in America not only for forage and the build-up of nitrates in the soil, but also because they are useful in checking soil erosion. One of these is the kudzu bean, *Pueraria lobota*, and the other type includes several species belonging to the genus *Lespedeza* that we call *lespedezas*. Actually, wild lespedeza plants are found in eastern North America as well as Asia, but so-called Japanese clover and Korean lespedeza are introduced types. Lespedezas are most commonly raised in our South at the present time.

The Nightshades

If there was no other reason, the nightshade family would be notable because it gave rise to the white or Irish potato. But in addition, this group includes the red peppers, belladonna plants, and henbane plants discussed in Chapter 4, tobacco which is dealt with in Chapter 5, as well as tomatoes and eggplants. So the nightshades have had considerable significance in human affairs.

The Potato Ireland Adopted. The Irish potato, *Solanum tuberosum*, has been a wanderer since it left its home in South America sometime during the sixteenth century. Presumably, the Incas had been raising it for a long time as a staple food, but it had not as yet been attached to Mayan or Aztec economy, and certainly was not raised by North American Indians despite certain fanciful tales that give such an impression. It is puzzling that maize was well known to all of the old American kingdoms, whereas the potato languished in rather localized obscurity.

The Spanish conquerors carried the Irish potato back to Europe, and later on the colonists transported it back across the ocean to our eastern seaboard. Subsequently it has been conveyed to nearly all parts of the world and has become a food plant of international consequence.

The potato that we eat is a swollen, underground tuber, bearing "eyes" which mark the location of buds. A portion of a tuber that bears one of these "eyes" can be used to raise a new potato plant. The species is quite hardy, can be grown on various soils provided there is enough moisture, and produces rewarding yields, although the food material is largely starch. Sugar, protein, and fat content are relatively low.

When the Irish potato arrived on the European scene, it received a mixed reception. There were some who thought that eating potatoes would lead to disease, and others who used potatoes in preparing "love philters." One account indicates that venturesome Italians began to raise and eat potatoes early in the seventeenth century. Apparently word got around that potatoes filled empty stomachs in a gratifying manner, and it was not long before they were being grown in northern Europe, as well as in both England and Ireland. In time, the Irish farmers came to depend upon this species as a principal crop. When their harvest was decimated by the disease known as late blight in the year 1845, a famine ensued and stimulated the emigration of Irish people to the new world.

The Russians did not begin to raise potatoes until some time in the eighteenth century, but today potatoes are produced in greatest quantity in northern Europe and the Soviet Union. This is in no small part due to the fact that potato tubers not only provide food, but serve as raw materials in the production of alcohol, vodka, starch, and other substances. Of course, potatoes are also popular in our own country, and in a recent year almost 300 million pounds were harvested (Fig. 2-3). A large portion of this crop became food for humans, but many so-called "culls" were used by industry and in feeding animals.

U.S.D.A. photo

Fig. 2-3. Digging potatoes is much easier when a mechanical harvester can be used.

The Notorious Love Apple. The history of the tomato, *Lycospersicon esculentum,* is not unlike that of the potato in some of its aspects. Wild ancestors of the tomato still grow in northern South America, and the plant was raised by both the Incas and the Aztecs. Explorers brought the tomato to Europe, and later on colonists conveyed it to the eastern coast of North America.

Tomatoes were first looked upon with grave suspicion by many Europeans. Their fruits, which are the portions that we eat, came to be known as "love apples" and were commonly said to be poisonous. This foolish idea persisted for many years among some Europeans and colonial Americans, who did raise tomatoes, but purely as ornamental plants. Back in the sixteenth century, however, some people along the

Mediterranean shore began to eat tomatoes, and after many years had passed, tomatoes gradually became accepted articles of diet.

It was later discovered that tomatoes were excellent sources of vitamins A and C, and lacking in the energy foods that many overweight people wished to avoid. Today, tomatoes are popular ingredients of salads, soups, relishes, pickles (green tomatoes), and the source of vast quantities of tomato juice and paste. The United States has become the principal tomato-producing country, but tomatoes are raised in many other lands, subject to the condition that they are sensitive to frosts. Many different varieties have been developed, including special hybrid types.

An Oversized Berry. An eggplant is about the last thing many people would call a berry. But from the scientific standpoint that is just what an eggplant is, and of course it is a fruit as well. Men have raised this species, *Solanum melongena*, for more than 4000 years; the custom of doing so developed either in south or Southeast Asia. Since the plant is not especially hardy, it is now grown largely in the warm-temperate and subtropical areas of the world. Several rather distinctive varieties have been developed in the course of time. In the United States, eggplants may be found in many home gardens, and large numbers are produced commercially, especially in the South.

The Mustard Group

The mustards include old world plants of the genus *Brassica* that have been cultivated in their homelands for many centuries. The three most important types are black, white, and Indian mustard, which have a long history of use as herbs and as sources of medicines and the seasoning substances we call condiments. At present, black mustard is raised to some extent in the United States, and the seeds are a source of commercial products including oils and adhesives. Black mustard tends to escape from cultivation, and often grows as a weed.

Another condiment plant of the mustard tribe is horse-radish, *Armoracia lapathifolia,* which seems to have begun its cultivated career in the Mediterranean area somewhat later than the mustards, and is raised for its root which is ground up to produce a familiar flavoring substance.

Cabbages and Their Relatives. The prize members of the mustard group are descended from the wild cabbage plant, *Brassica oleracea,* which is still found in the Mediterranean area. Apparently this plant was among the first cultivated types, and down through the years it has given rise to a whole series of descendants, including Brussels sprouts, broccoli, cab-bages of various types, cauliflower, collards, kales, and kohlrabi.

Cabbage plants are relatively hardy and can be raised in the colder countries of the world. While low in energy food value, they are good sources of needed vitamins and minerals. We consume them in soups and salads and as boiled vegeta-bles. We produce sauerkraut from head cabbage.

In addition, various members of the group, and especially a variety of kale, are raised in the colder lands to be used as livestock food. This practice is supported by the fact that crop yields are comparatively high, and this is also a reason why cabbage plants are such strong favorites in the diet of north Europeans.

The Turnips and Rutabagas. Turnips (*Brassica rapa*) and the closely related rutabagas also have a very long history of cultivation, which may have begun in the Mediterranean area. Like the cabbage plants they are hardy, and they are now grown extensively in the colder inhabited areas. Their bulbous roots and green tops serve to feed both man and some of the animals he raises. In the United States, however, they are of less importance than the members of the cabbage group.

Radishes of Many Colors. As cultivated plants, radishes (*Raphanus sativus*) do not appear to be as old as the cabbages and turnips. Probably they were first raised in central or Southeast Asia about 20 centuries ago, although a wild radish is resident in the Mediterranean area today. Radish roots are relatively low in food value, but serve useful functions as appetizers and in salads. Many varieties of winter and spring radishes have been developed, including types that are red, red and white, white, purple, and black.

Morning Glory and Yam Plants

A good many people seem to be confused about sweet potatoes and yams. These tuber-bearing plants are quite different. Yams were first cultivated at least 20 centuries ago somewhere in the southeast Asian area, and they are monocots of the yam family. Sweet potatoes, on the other hand, were cultivated in tropical America and perhaps even earlier, and they are dicots of the morning glory family.

The Old World Yams. Yams belong to a number of species in the genus *Discorea,* and develop tuberous roots that are very large in some cases. Sometimes the plants also have tubers on their vines. These yams have become popular in countries around the world, the tubers being cooked and eaten, and serving as the source of a flour or meal. Yams are grown to some extent in the southern part of the United States, but here they are regarded mainly as food for animals.

The New World Sweet Potatoes. The sweet potato, *Ipomoea batatas,* was under cultivation by the Incas, Mayans, and Aztecs before the coming of the Spaniards. It was also being raised on various islands in the vast Pacific Ocean domain before the first European explorers invaded the area. How the sweet potato reached these localities, including Hawaii, is one of the intriguing questions for which we may never have an answer. In more recent times, cultivation has been extended to the warmer areas of both the old and the new world. The sweet potato requires not only a mild, but also a moist climate, and at best, its yield does not seriously rival that of the Irish potato.

Nevertheless, sweet potatoes are a popular crop, and in tropical regions we are likely to find just about everyone raising them. In the United States, they are produced in the South, in quantities ranging from about 15 million to 45 million pounds per year. We eat them fresh, can or dehydrate them, use them as sources of starch, sugar, and alcohol, and fed them to livestock.

Several varieties of sweet potatoes exist, and they belong to two general groups. The cooked tubers of one group have a mealy texture and are pale yellow in color. Cooked tubers of the other group are more watery, are likely to be some shade of orange in color, and contain a notable amount of carotene. It is the latter group that is likely to be confused with the old world yams.

Some Tropical Roots and Tubers

Various tropical plants provide edible materials upon which native tribesmen have subsisted in part for countless years. Some of the tropical natives also learned to cultivate a number of useful species, many of them all but unknown to people who live in the colder parts of the world.

Taro Plants and Poi. If you had been raised a Polynesian you would be very familiar with the starchy food substance known as poi. It is made from the ground and fermented tubers of taro plants belonging to the genus *Colocasia* (Fig. 2-4). One theory holds that taro plants were first cultivated in the southeast Asian area, and that later the practice was extended to islands far out in the Pacific Ocean. As the inhabitants of these islands moved about in their sea-going outrigger canoes, they took taro plants with them.

Poi is not the only food product obtained from taro plants. Both the tubers and the leaves are prepared for the table in a variety of ways.

Taro plants belong to the arum family, and therefore are monocots. The so-called dasheens, which have been raised in our own South, are related to them. So are the yautia plants of the West Indies. The starchy roots are used like potatoes, and a flour-like substance is also made from them.

Cassavas and Tapioca. Cassavas or maniocs are quite unlike taro plants, except that they yield a root crop that has become even more popular than the sweet potato in tropical lands. They are members of the spurge family. Their history as cultivated plants appears to have begun with either Inca or Mayan farmers many centuries ago, and today there are two main species belonging to the genus *Manihot*, and many different varieties. The bitter cassava, *Manihot esculenta*, is now raised in a number of the warmer countries.

The roots of the bitter cassava are large and fleshy. When first removed from the soil, they contain the poison hydrocyanic acid, but this is driven off when heat is applied. The roots are then used to produce a type of meal known as farinha, and also the food substance called tapioca. The latter comes from the starch that is stored in the roots. In addition to foods, commercial starch and alcohol are derived from this species.

Two other tuber-producing plants that came out of Inca

Hawaii Visitors Bureau

Fig. 2-4. Early Polynesian migrants brought the ancestors of this taro plant to Hawaii.

gardens are oca (*Oxalis tuberosa*) and ullucu (*Ullucus tuberosus*). These plants are not closely related to the preceding types or to each other. They are still cultivated in their homeland, but have not been widely accepted in other parts of the world.

The Gourd Plants

The gourd family includes the chayote plant, cucumbers, gourds, pumpkins, muskmelons, squashes, and watermelons. These are vine plants that produce edible fruits.

The Chayote Plant.   The chayote plant is a native of tropical America and is a perennial of the species *Sechium edule*. It grows as a vine on the surface, but can also be trained to grow on a trellis, thus serving as an ornamental species. Fruits of the chayote are pear-shaped, with a white flesh inside. These fruits provide human food, as do the starchy roots of this plant. In addition, the vines may be used as forage for animals. The chayote plant, however, remains largely confined to its parent area.

Cucumbers for Pickles and Relishes. Supposedly the cucumber, *Cucumis sativus,* was first grown in what is now India. And clearly, this happened a long time ago. A number of varieties have been developed in the course of time, and all of them must have a relatively warm growing season. This has not, however, barred cucumbers from becoming popular plants around the world. Where they cannot be grown out-of-doors, they often are produced under glass. The fruits that we call cucumbers are used in relishes, salads, and pickles, and are also cooked in various combinations with other foods.

The Muskmelons. Muskmelons of the species *Cucumis melo* also have an ancient origin which seems to have been somewhere in Asia. Like cucumbers, they require a relatively warm growing season, and they are favored by a good supply of soil moisture. A number of special varieties have been developed, which are raised in both the old and the new world. These varieties differ in size, shape, and external markings. Muskmelons are a favorite commercial crop in some of the irrigated areas of the western and southwestern United States.

Pumpkins, Squashes, and Gourds. The pumpkins, squashes, and gourds belong to the genus *Curcubita,* and are represented by a variety of modern types. In years past, gourds were used to fashion bowls and other containers, but today they are raised largely as ornamentals. The other members of the group are primarily food plants that are grown in various parts of the world today. Some writers have suggested an African origin for pumpkins and squashes, but rather convincing evidence points to tropical America as their homeland. For when the European explorers reached the Americas they found the Incas, Mayans, Aztecs, and presumably the North American Indians raising these plants. So one might ask how the early Americans obtained them if the plants were not native.

In the old American kingdoms, pumpkins and squashes appear to have ranked next to maize and beans as staple food plants, a status that they do not maintain in the modern world. But they are raised in many countries, they have good keeping qualities, and some of them commonly find their way to our tables, although certain pumpkins are grown largely as animal food.

An Old African Custom. It is evident that natives of tropical Africa discovered the watermelon, *Citrullus vulgaris,* centuries ago. The plant was known in ancient Egypt, and later on was conveyed to many other parts of the world. Africans still favor watermelons, and elsewhere these fruits are commonly produced in southern Europe and Asia, and the southern part of North America. A number of special varieties are available to the farmer. For the most part, the melons are eaten fresh, but their rinds are also pickled and used in preparing various relishes.

The Goosefoot Plants

Two of our cultivated vegetable types come from the goosefoot family of flowering plants. They are the beets and the spinach plants.

Garden Beets.   Somewhere in the Mediterranean area men began to raise beets a long time ago. These plants belong to the species *Beta vulgaris.* The most primitive type of modern beet is chard, which no doubt gave rise to the mangels that are often grown as animal food in the old world. But garden beets were also developed and are now represented by many varieties in different parts of the world, widespread distribution being possible because these plants are fairly hardy. Garden beets serve largely as human food, being eaten fresh (boiled), pickled, canned, and quick frozen. Beets are usually called a root crop, but their leaves are also boiled and eaten.

The Spinach Plant.   Young people whose parents constantly urge them to eat spinach sometimes regard this plant as a noxious weed. But spinach has become a popular green vegetable in many lands. A probably wild ancestor has not been found in nature, but it is theorized that the cultivated form came from southwestern Asia.

Spinach plants are quite hardy, and grow best on fairly moist soils and in cool weather. We eat the leaves of these plants, which are generally available in fresh, canned, or quick-frozen form.

Edible Lily Plants

You may regard the lily group as one which includes a number of ornamental plants. And so it does, but along with them you find other species that we eat, including asparagus, chives, onions, shallots, and the odoriferous, all-pervading garlic.

Asparagus, a Spring Vegetable.   Asparagus, or *Asparagus officinalis,* is still found growing wild in Europe and Asia. It is believed that people in the Mediterranean area began its cultivation some time before the dawn of the Christian Era. Now the plant is raised in various parts of the world, including North America.

It takes four or five years to get an asparagus bed started from seed; after that, the shoots that we eat spring up from underground parts for another 15 to 20 years. Asparagus is generally eaten fresh, but some of the commercial crop is either canned or quick frozen.

Onions and Their Relatives. Asparagus has no strong or offensive odor, but the members of the genus *Allium* are likely to make their presence known even in the gloom of night. The onion, *Allium cepa,* probably was the first representative of this genus to be cultivated. Various evidences indicate that the onion was grown in the Mediterranean area or western Asia over 40 centuries ago. It is a hardy biennial that keeps well in storage, and is widely used to prepare many dishes. Many varieties of onions are now available, and most of them are well adapted to growth in colder parts of temperate regions.

The shallot, *Allium ascalonicum,* is a perennial that resembles the onion in structure, having underground bulbs and leaves that form hollow cylinders above ground. Its uses are similar to those of the onion, but it is more of a favorite in Europe than in America.

Chives (*Allium schoenoprasum*) grow wild in northern Europe and Asia. They are also found in many gardens of temperate areas. Chives are very hardy perennials that grow in bunches. Small underground bulbs give rise to the slender, hollow, green cylinders that appear above ground. Both the shoots and the bulbs are used to season foods.

Garlic (*Allium sativum*) is an Asian plant, which produces groups of small, underground bulbs known as "cloves." In times past, garlic has been used as a drug, and still is to some extent. Otherwise, it serves to season foods in no uncertain fashion, and is practically a "must" in the Italian and French cuisines, although its use is by no means limited to these countries.

Other Vegetables and Condiments

The Parsley Plants. The parsley family has contributed a number of herbs used in seasoning, as well as vegetables. Among the herb plants are angelica, anise, caraway, parsley, and dill. More substantial food is provided by the carrots, celery plants, and parsnips.

Wild celery (*Apium graveolens*) still grows in both Europe and Asia. Over 20 centuries ago some people began its cultivation, and this has led to the development of many varieties, including even an old world type that has red stems. In America, the stems usually are blanched white by depriving them of light during the latter part of their growing period. Celery plants require a fairly good soil and plenty of moisture. They have become popular in many lands for use in salads, soups, and stews. Celery seeds are also widely employed to flavor foods.

The history of the carrot is similar to that of celery. Apparently it was first cultivated at about the same time as celery, either in the Mediterranean area or western Asia. The wild source is *Daucus carota*, which now grows as a weed in northern Europe and North America. There are numerous cultivated varieties of carrots, and some of them are grown more or less throughout the world. Carrots are popular items in salads, soups, and stews, and it is worthy of note that they contain substantial amounts of carotene.

Parsnips (*Pastinica sativa*) were attached to human food economy at a somewhat later date than celery or carrots. Probably they too come from the Mediterranean area or from western Asia. In some localities, they grow as weeds, but cultivated varieties are found in fields and gardens of both the old and the new world. Like carrots, parsnips are a root crop. A good many parsnips serve as human food, but a portion of the annual crop is fed to livestock.

Composites and Salads. The composite family contributes a number of items to human diet, largely in the form of salad plants. Even the dandelion, *Taraxacum officinale*, which is a pest to home owners who are trying to develop solid stands of bluegrass on their lawns, has been gathered and used as greens for centuries, and in later years has even been raised for the market.

The prize member of the composite group is the lettuce plant, *Lactuca sativa*, which was taken under cultivation many centuries ago either in the Mediterranean area or in western Asia. Wild lettuce appears today in both the old world and the new, but the many cultivated varieties are clearly descendants of old world stock. Various types of head lettuce are ranking favorites in the markets, but other types that do not form heads are produced in many home gardens.

The endive plant, *Cichorium endiva*, may be of more recent cultivation, although it has been an old world favorite for a long time, and seems to be achieving greater popularity in America as time goes on. It is, of course, another salad plant, similar to lettuce in its uses, and probably raised first in southern Asia.

Chicory, *Cichorium intybus*, is a relative newcomer as a cultivated plant, and it grows as a weed both in Europe and North America. It is raised as a salad plant, but also because its roasted roots are mixed with ground coffee beans to produce a coffee that is especially popular in Europe.

The salsify plant, which is *Tragopogon porrifolius*, belongs in this same composite group, but is used in a different fashion. Supposedly, it came from the Mediterranean area, where early gardeners learned to prize its fleshy roots as ingredients of soups and stews. When the roots are cooked in milk, the product has a flavor not unlike oyster stew, and this is the reason why salsify is sometimes called the "oyster plant."

Old World Peppers. The red or capsicum peppers are of new world origin, and belong to the nightshade family. Inasmuch as they are used in concocting various medicines, the reader will find them discussed in Chapter 4. Black peppers and long peppers, however, are members of the pepper family, and the types we cultivate go back more than 20 centuries to a southeast Asian origin.

Both the black and white peppers of commerce come from the fruits or berries of *Piper nigrum*, a vine-like perennial which can be trained as a climber on trees or poles. This plant is now raised in southeast Asia, the Philippines, islands in the South Pacific, the West Indies, and Africa. But in the early days of commerce and trade, the medieval Europeans, who had embraced pepper with enthusiasm, had to obtain this condiment from the Indies, and it was by far the most important commodity in the "spice trade."

Substance	Nature of plant source	Portion of plant used	Uses of product
Allspice	tree	fruit	flavoring, perfumes
Angelica	herb	roots, stems, fruits	flavoring, perfumes, medicines
Basil	herb	leaves	flavoring, perfumes
Caraway	herb	fruit	flavoring, perfumes, medicines
Cassia	tree	bark, buds	flavoring, perfumes, medicines
Cinnamon	tree	bark	flavoring, medicines
Cloves	tree	flower buds	flavoring, medicines
Coriander	herb	fruit	flavoring
Dill	herb	seeds, leaves	flavoring, medicines
Fennel	herb	entire plant	flavoring, perfumes, medicines
Ginger	herb	roots	flavoring, medicines
Juniper	tree	fruit	flavoring
Nutmeg	tree	seeds	flavoring, medicines
Peppermint	herb	leaves	flavoring, medicines
Sage	herb	leaves	flavoring, perfumes, medicines
Sarsaparilla	vine	roots	flavoring
Spearmint	herb	leaves	flavoring, medicines
Thyme	shrub	leaves	flavoring, perfumes, medicines
Turmeric	herb	tubers	flavoring, food coloring
Wintergreen	tree	bark	flavoring, medicines
Vanilla	herb	fruit	flavoring

Table 2-1.   The sources of flavoring substances derived from plants.

Peppercorns that we sometimes grind at the table in small pepper mills, are simply the dried fruits of *Piper nigrum*. The black pepper of our markets is made by grinding peppercorns which were picked and dried before they were ripe. If the fruits are allowed to ripen further, and their outer portions removed, the remaining materials may be ground to yield white pepper. To some extent these old world peppers are still used in certain medicines, but this is greatly overshadowed by their popularity as condiments.

Two types of long peppers from the southeast Asian area also belong to the genus *Piper*, but not to the same species. They are grown as sources of condiments in India, the East Indies, and the Philippines, but have never attained the world-

ʾwide popularity of the black and white peppers. An African pepper known as ashanti also owes its origin to the genus *Piper*.

Other Flavoring Substances. A large number of plants provide substances that are used in flavoring foods, and not enough space is available to discuss them in detail. A supplementary list, however, is shown in Table 2-1, together with data about sources and the nature of products. The reader may note that a good many substances listed in Table 2-1 are used in compounding medicines, but this does not necessarily mean that they are the substances in the medicines that are supposed to have curative powers. Sometimes they serve merely to provide flavor.

3

Fruits and Nuts

What the housewife calls a "fruit," and what the botanist means when he says "fruit" are likely to be quite different things. To the botanist, a number of plant foods that have already been discussed in Chapter 2 are fruits. For example, a green bean pod is a fruit, and within it we find the fruit's seeds. A cereal product such as a wheat grain is really a one-seeded fruit. Tomatoes, eggplants, and melons are all fruits. These fruits are developed from ovaries and some associated parts of flowers, and in many cases we expect to find seeds in them (Fig. 3-1).

A nut is sometimes a one-seeded dry fruit, which has a hard outer covering or shell. In some other cases, the shell encloses a seed rather than a fruit.

Men obtain useful fruits from a number of trees, bushes, and other plants. In tropical regions, some of these fruits are staple articles of human fare and are relied upon to provide energy supplies needed by the human body. In temperate areas, however, the fruits that we raise are prized for their minerals, vitamins, and flavors, rather than as sources of energy, for most of them rank low in the latter respect. An apple pie contains a good deal of energy food to be sure, but this comes from the flour, sugar, and related materials, rather than from the apples.

People have been raising some fruits for a long time, both in the old world and the new. Thus the Europeans learned to cultivate one species of strawberry on their side of the world, while Inca farmers had learned to cultivate another species in northern South America. As usual, the origins of some of our cultivated fruits are obscured by the passage of time and by the lack of written records.

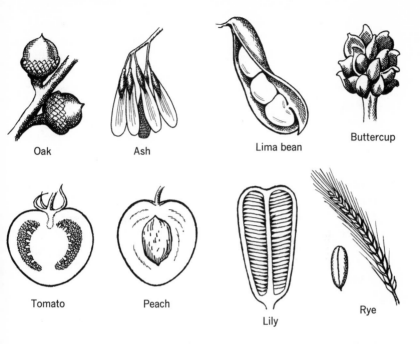

Oak Ash Lima bean Buttercup

Tomato Peach Lily Rye

Fig. 3-1. The fruits of various plants.

Fruits from the Rose Family

Strangely enough, many of the fruits that prosper in temperate areas come from members of the rose family, which includes the almonds, apples, apricots, blackberries, cherries, loganberries, nectarines, peaches, pears, plums, quinces, raspberries, and strawberries.

The Old Apple Tree. In the early days of the nineteenth century, a wandering border character named Jonathan Chapman, but more commonly known as "Johnny Appleseed," made a series of journeys across the Alleghenies and into the lands beyond, bearing supplies of apple seeds which he planted for the benefit of both the native Indians and white families living on the frontier. He continued this self-appointed activity for almost half a century, and became one of the legendary figures of what were then the borderlands.

Apples belong to the species *Pyrus malus,* and it is believed that men in eastern Europe or southwest Asia began to cultivate them over 30 centuries ago. The first cultivated apples in North America probably were planted in what is now our Southwest, although apple trees appeared along the eastern seacoast before many more years had passed. In time, apples became the leading fruit crop of the United States and Canada, because among other reasons, apple trees are capable of surviving in the colder temperate climates, although the apple crop can be damaged by frosts.

Many different varieties of apples have been developed by the plant experimenters. There are summer apples, fall apples, winter apples, red apples, yellow apples, green apples, big apples, little apples, sweet apples, and sour apples; in fact, apples to meet almost any reasonable demand. Hybridization and selection have been the primary techniques employed in developing the various types.

As fruit trees go, apple trees are relatively long lived. They can be sprouted from seeds, and shoots of a desired type can be grafted on rootstocks of other varieties. The apples produced by some types keep well in storage, and this has been a factor that assured their popularity in past years. But even in these days of fast transportation, refrigeration, and tin cans, apples continue to hold first rank. The commercial apple crop of the United States approximated 130 million bushels in a recent year, which takes no account of the many apples produced for home consumption. The commercial crop came largely from Washington, New York, Michigan, and California.

We eat apples as they come to us from the trees, but we also dry and can them, or extract their fluid content to make jellies, cider, and applejack. Apple pie has become an American institution, and applesauce is still welcomed on many tables.

Peaches. The cultivation of peaches (*Prunus persica*) evidently began in the southeast Asian area thousands of years ago. To be sure, the specific name *persica* suggests Persia as the place of origin, but Persia probably was just a stopping off point as the peach began its long journey from east to west. Peach trees blossomed in Europe before the beginning of the Christian Era, and post-Columbian explorers, including the Spanish, brought them to the new world.

The peach tree is shorter lived and lacks the hardiness of the apple. Peach fruits do not store as well as apples, but they lend themselves well to canning, drying, and freezing, and they commonly appear in pies, short cakes, and ice creams.

In this group of rose plants, peach production ranks second to that of apples in the United States, where about 78 million bushels of peaches were produced in a recent year. Leading peach states were California, South Carolina, Georgia, and Pennsylvania, but we find many peach trees in states farther to the north. Other world centers of production include the Orient, southern Europe, Australia, and Africa. If the reader wonders where nectarines fit into this picture, they are really varieties of peaches which have fruits with smooth outer surfaces.

F.S.N.B.

Fig. 3-2. Power spraying of trees in a Florida citrus grove.

Pears with Two Ancestors, and the Related Quince. Like apples, pears belong to the genus *Pyrus*, but some of the pears that we raise in America today are hybrids produced by crossing two related species. One of these species is *Pyrus communis*, which has been cultivated for a long time by peoples of Europe and western Asia and apparently was even known to stone age men. It is, of course, a close relative of the apple tree, but is somewhat less hardy. The pear tree is still popular in Europe, and is raised in some parts of the United States, Africa, South America, and Australia.

Pears came along with apples, peaches, and other old world plants that early colonists brought to North America. In some parts of the new land, however, the pear did not prosper because of a disease called fire blight. But another blight-resistant pear grew well in these areas; this was the sand pear, *Pyrus pyrifolia*, an Asiatic type whose fruit contained many grit cells, but had good keeping qualities. Almost inevitably, the European pear was crossed with the sand pear to produce hybrids that also resist fire blight. These hybrids, however, retain somewhat more grit cells in their fruits than most pear-eating enthusiasts would approve.

As matters stand in the United States today, *Pyrus communis* is raised in some localities where fire blight is not a problem, and hybrid varieties are raised in other areas. A good deal of the commercial crop is eaten fresh or is canned. In a recent year, this crop amounted to almost 30 million bushels, largely from California, Oregon, Washington, and Michigan.

The quince, *Cydonia oblonga*, is a first cousin of the pear. It is believed to have come from southern Asia, and was quite popular among early American colonists. It is not, however, one of the favorite American fruits today, probably because so many other types of fruits have become readily available. Quinces are generally used to concoct various jellies and preserves.

Plums, Prunes, and Preserves. Plum fruits come in various shades of green, yellow, red, blue, and purple. There are, as a matter of fact, several species and many varieties of plums in the modern world, and some of them have been cultivated for thousands of years. Some of the wild ancestors of plums were native to the old world, and others were native to North America.

There is some doubt about the matter, but the so-called European plum, *Prunus domestica,* probably hails from western Asia. It was a fruit of the ancient Greeks and Romans and was conveyed to North America during the early days of settlement. Among the many varieties of this species, which include most of the commercial plums, are the prune plums, as well as other types that are generally eaten fresh or used to make preserves. In a recent year, over 400 thousand tons of prunes were produced in the United States, largely in California, Oregon, Washington, and Idaho.

Generally speaking, a prune is a dried plum that has rather high sugar content. After being dried, the fruits are processed to give them a shiny appearance. Prunes have, of course, been popular winter fruits, especially a generation or two ago when they occupied a conspicuous place in village stores, along with the cracker barrel and the inevitable cake of cheese. We can see from the figures quoted above that they still find a ready market.

The damson plum, *Prunus insititia,* is another species that doubtless came from southern Europe or western Asia, where it still grows wild. This plum tree produces a rather small, rounded fruit that is largely used in making preserves. It has been raised in the old world for centuries and is now found in a good many American home orchards.

Wild, native plum trees grew in abundance in the America of pioneer days. The common type was *Prunus americana,* but some other species were also represented. These plums blossomed relatively late and thus escaped a good deal of potential frost damage. We find their descendants in a good many farm orchards today.

Toward the end of the past century, the plum species *Prunus salicina,* imported from Japan, had considerable vogue. It is sometimes called the Oriental plum, and it is believed to have come from the Asiatic mainland. Like other plum species, this one is represented by many varieties, some of which are raised commercially.

Apricots to Dry and to Can.   Apricots of the species *Prunus armeniaca* are thought to have been cultivated in China some 4000 years ago, and to have spread westward across southern Asia to the Mediterranean area. Their scientific name suggests an Armenian origin, but the reader has already learned to be wary of such names and their implications. Apricots do not fare well in a land of frosts, but the early Spanish settlers brought them to Mexico and California, where they soon became established.

Dried apricots are a familiar sight in food stores, and canned apricots are generally available. Most of the commercial crop is marketed in these two forms, but some of it serves as fresh fruit or is used to produce juice. In a recent year, production of apricots in the United States totaled about 150 thousand tons, and leading production centers were California, Washington, and Utah.

Sweet, Sour, and Wild Cherries.   The rose family includes the cherries, which are represented by wild species in both the old and the new world. The native wild, black cherry, *Prunus serotina*, bears a small fruit that is often used in making wines and preserves, but in common with other cherries of American origin, it does not have the commercial importance enjoyed by cultivated cherries from the old world.

The old world fruits of this type include sweet cherries that we are disposed to eat as they come to us from the trees, and sour cherries that we employ to make cherry pies. The sweet cherries are *Prunus avium*, and sour cherries are *Prunus cerasus*. The big black cherries that we see on fruit stands in early summer are sweet cherries. Sour cherries are more likely to be canned or frozen when they reach the market. One theory holds that both of these old world species originated in western Asia and southeastern Europe; at any rate, cultivation was begun a long time ago, and sweet cherries were known to stone age Europeans. Probably sour cherries were not as popular centuries ago; to appreciate them we must be able to make cherry pie.

The colonists brought cherries to eastern North America, and the Spaniards established them on the West Coast. Like apples, cherries do well in cool, temperate areas, but both sweet and sour types are likely to suffer spring frost damage. Many special varieties have been developed, both in America and in Europe. As in the case of other fruits, such varieties result from chance variation, hybridization, and selection.

The American appetite for cherries seems to be substantial. The commercial crop in a recent year amounted to about 300 thousand tons, and the leading states in this production were Michigan, Oregon, California, and New York. The flowering cherries that are responsible for "cherry blossom time" in Washington, D.C. and some other American cities are mostly members of the Oriental species *Prunus serrulata*, which is raised as an ornamental.

Strawberries and Short Cakes. Strawberries are small, perennial herbs which are represented in the native floras of both the old and the new world. Centuries ago, Europeans undoubtedly ate fruits of the species *Fragaria vesca*, but apparently made no serious effort to cultivate these plants until medieval times.

In northern South America, however, the old Inca farmers were raising *Fragaria chiloensis*, and in the eighteenth century some representatives of this species were taken to Europe. About a century earlier, *Fragaria virginiana*, which was abundant as a wild plant in eastern North America, had been transported to many European gardens.

Once the business of raising strawberries got underway, the processes of crossing and selection resulted in the production of many new varieties. Some of our modern strawberries probably represent crosses between *Fragaria chiloensis* and *Fragaria virginiana*. Others are varieties derived from *Fragaria chiloensis* alone. At any rate, strawberries have become very popular, both in home gardens and as a commercial crop. Strawberry growers in our own country produced over 250 thousand tons of these fruits in a recent year.

Some of the enthusiasm for strawberries doubtless relates to the fact that they can be used in so many different ways.

Many of them are eaten fresh with cream, in ice creams, and in strawberry short cakes. Part of the crop is frozen, part of it is canned, and part of it goes into a variety of strawberry preserves.

Raspberries and Blackberries. Our European forbears were eating the fruits of red raspberries (*Rubus ideaus*) centuries ago, and somewhere along the way they began to plant these briars in their gardens. When the colonists came to North America, they found a similar red raspberry growing in the new land, and also a black raspberry known as *Rubus occidentalis.* The colonists also encountered various species of blackberries, which are closely related, being members of the same genus *Rubus.*

Cultivation of the black raspberries and the blackberries began in relatively recent times, and various types have been produced by crossing and selecting. The fruits are not of first-rank importance, but raspberries in particular are hardy and will survive as far north as the Arctic Circle. Fruits of these plants are eaten fresh, used as sources of juices, and converted into jellies and preserves, or simply canned.

As most of you know, blackberries and raspberries, whether wild or cultivated, have a penchant for growing in clumps or masses that are all but impenetrable because of the short but sharp spines the plants bear. So the bramble patches that they develop provide ideal cover for a number of small animals. Many a cottontail rabbit, for instance, owes its continued existence to the briar patch in which it takes refuge when eluding its enemies.

The Vine Plants

The vine family is not as well represented as the rose family by fruits that we raise, but it includes the grapes, which have played a part in historical events in both ancient and modern times. The reader may recall that it was the souring of French wines that spread consternation through the vineyards and set Louis Pasteur on the trail of the elusive microbes.

Grapes, Wines, and Champagnes. Natives of the old world probably began to raise grapes over 100 centuries ago, possibly in western Asia. These were wine grapes of the species *Vitis vinifera,* and the Romans, who liked an occasional nip of fermented grape juice, transported grapes around the Roman world in the wake of their conquests. And even before the first Roman legion marched, the Egyptians were raising grapes in North Africa.

Other species of grapes were native to North America, and when the Vikings reached what probably was the coast of Labrador, they named it Vineland because they were so struck by the abundance of wild grapes. Hundreds of years later, settlers attempted to establish European grapes in the eastern colonies, but met with little success, although the same grapes would grow in California and on other continents. Why did the European grape plantings in the eastern colonies wither and die? In time, the answer was forthcoming in the form of an American insect that attacked grape roots. Native American grapes did not succumb to these attacks. All this became evident after the insect had made its way to Europe and was threatening the vineyards of that continent. The remedy, of

Standard Oil Co., N.J.

Fig. 3-3. A vineyard in southern France at harvest time. These are wine grapes.

course, was plain enough: all that was necessary was to graft European grapes on American rootstocks, which the wine producers soon learned to do both here and abroad.

Meanwhile, in eastern North America, the cultivation of native grapes had been undertaken, involving several species of the genus *Vitis,* and especially the fox grape (*Vitis labrusca*), and the muscadine grape (*Vitis rotundifolia*). Numerous varieties, including hybrid types have been developed through the years. The Concord grape, for example, was produced by crossing two native wild grapes and selecting from the progeny a type which bore large fruits of the desired quality.

On our West Coast today, most of the commercial grapes come from the old European stock, which is preferred because of the keeping and shipping qualities of the fruit. But this species is not very successful in some other areas of the country, where for the most part hardier varieties derived from native grapes are raised.

As for the fruits, various grapes are eaten fresh, and some varieties are preferred for wine making, others for preserves, and some are dried to become rasins. Certain light-colored wines are induced to ferment again after they have been sealed up in bottles. When the bottles are opened subsequently, the contents effervesce and we have what is known as champagne.

Over 3 million tons of grapes were produced in the United States in a recent year, most of them coming from California, New York, Michigan, and Washington. This, however, represents only a fraction of world production, for grapes are grown on all continents, and in parts of the Mediterranean area we see vineyards on every hand.

The Citrus Tribe

Unlike grapes and members of the rose family, citrus trees and bushes thrive only in tropical and semitropical environments. They have expanding use and popularity today, largely because better means have been developed for conveying the fruits and fruit juices to world markets. Some of the citrus species have been cultivated in their homeland for centuries, but it is only in recent times that most of them have become generally available.

Sweet and Sour Oranges. Sour oranges (*Citrus aurantium*) and sweet oranges (*Citrus sinensis*) came out of the southeast Asian area. For some reason the sour oranges were the first to be raised by Europeans along the shores of the Mediterranean Sea. These oranges are not the type we just pick and eat; rather, we use them to make marmalade and other preserves. Apparently sour oranges were first carried from India to North Africa, then to Europe, and after the voyages of Columbus, Spaniards established them in the West Indies and the land that is now Florida.

Apparently Florida was a good spot for sour oranges, and before long many of the trees had escaped from cultivation. Meanwhile, Europeans had tardily become aware that sweet

Sunkist photo

Fig. 3-4. Picking navel oranges in a southern California grove.

oranges existed, and were in many ways more pleasing to the palate. So early settlers in Florida were soon busily grafting sweet orange shoots on sour orange rootstocks. As a result, Florida had an abundance of sweet oranges long before there was an effective way to transport them to the big markets. The coming of the railroads provided the first solution for this problem and another means of shipping was provided when highway systems were developed.

Years ago, orange trees were also planted in the warmer parts of South America, and in Brazil an event occurred which had far-reaching consequences. One branch on a Brazilian tree was found to bear large, seedless oranges. Twigs from this branch were grafted on other orange stock, and before long the seedless, navel orange became an established variety. Navel orange trees were brought to California and other areas of the West, where they prospered. In our Southwest, two main varieties of oranges are produced today: navel oranges in the winter, and a type of sweet orange that contains seeds during the summer.

A third type of orange to come out of the Orient was the mandarin, *Citrus reticulata*. Like the sweet orange, the mandarin was brought to Europe long after the advent of sour oranges. Some varieties of mandarin oranges are what we now call tangerines. Anyone who has eaten tangerines knows that they have loose-fitting outer jackets and that they may be easily peeled. This is one reason why they have achieved considerable popularity as fruits that we eat fresh.

Mandarin oranges are still raised in their homeland. The United States has become the leading producer of sweet oranges, which are also grown extensively in Brazil, southern Europe, North Africa, and Mexico. In a recent year, the United States orange crop was about 150 million boxes, which came largely from Florida, California, Arizona, and Texas.

Captain Shaddock and His Seeds. Some time toward the end of the seventeenth century, an English sea captain is said to have collected some citrus seeds in the southeast Asian area, and carried them around the horn to the West Indies on his voyage to England. In fact, shaddock trees (*Citrus grandis*), which grow in the West Indian region and produce very large fruits, bear the name of this nebulous captain. But of course, the shaddock and the grapefruit (*Citrus paradisi*) are not the same species, although they are closely related. Yet grapefruit trees were growing in the West Indies by the middle of the eighteenth century.

Where did the grapefruit trees come from? Were they represented among the seeds brought in by Captain Shaddock? The probable answer is no, because wild grapefruit trees have not been reported from the East Indies or the Asiatic mainland. Do the grapefruits represent a cross between orange and shaddock trees? Again, this seems dubious, because the progeny of grapefruit trees do not exhibit the characteristics we normally associate with hybrids. What does this leave us? Well, it leaves us with the further possibility that the grapefruit tree originated in the West Indies as a mutation of the shaddock. Anyway, the record is not clear, even though the events we are describing occurred in relatively recent times.

Perhaps more attention would have been paid to the origin of the grapefruit tree if its potential importance had been appreciated back in the eighteenth century. As it was, the trees that sprang up in the West Indies attracted no special notice as sources of food, except on the part of the natives. About a century later, the grapefruit tree was conveyed to Florida, where for the time being it was mostly an exotic, experimental curiosity.

During the nineteenth century, Florida citrus growers selected special varieties of grapefruit not so burdened with seeds as some other varieties, and here and there people began to eat the new fruit. Near the close of the century, the grapefruit began to be a popular item with at least a portion of the public.

Like oranges and lemons, grapefruits are good sources of needed vitamins, and this fact has accelerated their general acceptance as fresh fruit and a source of fruit juice. Large amounts of grapefruit are also canned or frozen. New varieties have been developed, featuring a reddish pulp and further reduction in the number of seeds. We still raise more oranges than grapefruits in the United States, but during a recent year, over 40 million boxes of grapefruits were produced, largely in Florida, California, Arizona, and Texas. There also are plantings in southwest Asia, Africa, and the West Indies, but the market demand in other lands does not approach that of the United States.

Sailing Ships and Limeys. Back in the days of sailing ships and long voyages, scurvy was a common affliction of men who followed the seafaring life. In 1747, it was discovered that scurvy could be avoided by eating fresh oranges or lemons. Actually, all citrus fruits contain the scurvy-preventing vitamin C, although not in the same amounts. In time, the use of limes or lemons became such an established custom on English ships that British sailors were often called "limeys," and sometimes are so-called today.

Lemons contain much vitamin C, and also vitamins A, B, and G. Limes contain vitamin C also, but not as much as we find in lemons, oranges, or grapefruits. Just the same, limes became famous as antiscorbutics.

The lemon tree, *Citrus limon,* is a small, and sometimes bush-like species, that probably was first cultivated in the southeast Asian area. In that part of the world there are sweet as well as sour lemons, but it is the sour types that have become popular in other lands. Some of these sour varieties probably are hybrids, and for this reason they are generally propagated by grafting, so that the new trees will bear the same fruits as the trees from which the grafts came.

Lemon trees were carried westward across southern Asia, and reached Mediterranean shores in pre-Christian times. They are not as hardy as oranges, but on the other hand, they do not fare very well in a moist, hot climate, because in such an environment they are likely to be beset by parasitic fungi. The Spaniards brought lemon trees to the West Indies in the fifteenth century, and to Central America, Mexico, and California somewhat later. It was not until recent times, however, that lemon production became an important American industry. About 15 million boxes represents the current level of production, most of them coming from California and Arizona. A good many lemons are also raised in parts of southern Europe.

Lemon pulp provides juice for beverages, and also is a source of citric acid. The lemon rinds yield lemon oil used in flavoring, and pectin, which has medical uses, and also is employed to make jellies or other preserves. It should be noted, however, that commercial sources of pectin include other citrus fruits and apples.

The lime tree is *Citrus aurantifolia,* another relatively small tree that is inclined to be bushy. It requires a warm, subtropical environment, and in such a setting it may tend to escape from cultivation. Probably men first raised limes in the East Indies. Both sweet and sour varieties exist in the homeland, but the sour types are the ones we see in world markets.

The Spaniards brought limes to the new world in the sixteenth century, and they are raised today in Mexico, the West Indies, Florida, and California. Portions of North Africa are also important in lime production. The fruits serve largely to provide beverages, and as a source of citric acid.

Citrus Fruits of Lesser Importance. Small trees or shrubs of the genus *Fortunella* produce the little citrus fruits known as kumquats. Their cultivation was begun in the southeast Asian area centuries ago, and they are fairly hardy representatives of the citrus group. Both the pulp and rind of a kumquat fruit may be eaten, and the fruits can also be candied or used in making preserves.

Kumquats remained largely in their homeland until the middle of the nineteenth century when they were conveyed to both Europe and North America. They are raised in the warmer parts of our country both as ornamentals and as sources of fruit.

The citron (*Citrus medica*) is another small citrus tree, but it produces fruits about six inches long. Like limes and lemons, these fruits come in both sweet and sour varieties. The citron also has been cultivated for a long time in the southeast Asian area, and probably was the first member of the citrus group to reach the shores of the Mediterranean, where it is still something of a favorite. It also is raised to a limited extent in tropical America. The candied rind is the portion of the fruit that is important; this rind is marketed under the name citron.

The Heath Plants

We now come to a group of fruit-bearing plants that are native, and like some members of the rose family, are able to survive in the colder lands. These are members of the heath family, which includes the cranberries, blueberries, and huckleberries. Cranberries are vine-like; blueberries and huckleberries grow as shrubs or bushes.

Cranberries, Bear Meat, and Pemmican. Indians of the Northeast were familiar with *Vaccinium macrocarpum,* the native cranberry, long before white men set foot on these shores. They ground up cranberries and sun dried meat, together with animal fat, to form pemmican, a substance that would sustain life and could be transported easily when the Indians were on the move. The cranberries served primarily to flavor the mixture.

Pemmican did not become a popular food with the colonists, but they soon learned to eat cooked cranberries, and for a long time got their supplies from wild plants that grew in abundance around some of the bogs. Soon after the nineteenth century began, however, there were pioneer efforts to cultivate the native cranberry, and ultimately they were successful. Cranberry cultivation, however, is more or less limited to New England and north central states, where in a recent year over 3 million cases of the canned berries were produced.

Blueberries and Huckleberries. Eastern North America was also well supplied with blueberries belonging to several species of the genus *Vaccinium,* and so were some localities along the West Coast. Other blueberries are native to Europe, Asia, and South America. Some of these plants can withstand arctic cold, and others thrive in the tropics. But they seem to have one common requirement: an acid soil such as that which develops on some forest floors.

The related huckleberries belong to the genus *Gaylussacia,* and contain large seeds, whereas the seeds of both low bush and high bush blueberries are so small that they are likely to be unnoticed when the fruits are eaten. But people are inclined to become confused about these plants, and many an individual says "huckleberry," when he really means "blueberry."

Blueberries are favorites with various native birds, and the fruit crop sometimes gets picked by our feathered friends as fast as it ripens. The simple way to deal with this problem is to raise enough blueberries to keep the birds oversupplied.

The colonists found blueberries very acceptable as fruit in season, and for many years farmers who happened to have natural growths of blueberry bushes have picked blueberries for home use and for the market. In fact, this practice is still followed even in these days of blueberry pies, canned blueberries, and frozen blueberries. But about 50 years ago, the possibility of developing superior varieties began to receive attention, and it has led to the production of fruits considerably larger than the wild types.

Popular Fruits from the Warmer Lands

We have previously considered some tropical and subtropical fruits of the citrus group. But there are other fruit-producing species that prosper only in the warmer countries. These plants belong to a number of different families, and are native to various parts of the earth. Some of their fruits are commonly seen in our own markets; others are less well known, at least for the moment.

The Succulent Fig. The important commercial species of fig is *Ficus carica,* a member of the mulberry family. Records indicate that it was cultivated at a relatively early date, probably somewhere in southwest Asia. It is a small, bushy tree, which can be propagated from cuttings. Long before the Christian Era began, fig groves had been established in the Mediterranean area including North Africa. In the course of time, variation and selection have provided the world with many fig varieties, including the seedless common figs, the Smyrna figs, and the San Pedro figs.

Fig fruits have a high sugar content, and the small seeds found in some types do not interfere materially with the pleasures of eating. Figs are now raised in warm countries around the world, including some areas of our Southwest. They were brought to the western world by the Spaniards in the sixteenth century, and appear in many home orchards of our warmer states.

Commercial fig raising in the Southwest got off to a slow start in the latter part of the nineteenth century. This was largely because efforts were being made to raise Smyrna figs, which must receive pollen from wild figs if they are to produce fruits. Moreover, a small fig wasp must be present to do the job of pollinating. Once this became known, wild figs and fig wasps were imported, and the fig-raising industry began to prosper.

The Banana. The banana is the primary fruit of tropical areas, but it was not until comparatively recent times that people who live in colder lands made its acquaintance. The banana plant is *Musa sapientum,* a member of a family which includes the bananas and plantains. It is really an herb, but one that may grow to a height of 30 feet or more under cultivation, and to the non-scientist, appears to be a tree (Fig. 3-5).

Bananas may be one of the oldest of the economic plants. As might be expected, it is not known where or how cultivation began, but certainly bananas were raised in southern Asia and tropical Africa centuries ago. From the southeast Asian area plants were conveyed to islands of the South Pacific at an early date. In the sixteenth century, bananas were brought to the West Indies, and before long, were being raised in other parts of tropical America. Many different varieties have been developed under cultivation, including some that are red when they have ripened.

It is easy to understand why bananas have become so popular in the warm countries. They can be raised from portions of underground stems, and given a favorable environment, will grow rapidly. They produce fruits in bunches, which are harvested while still green, and then allowed to ripen en route to market. Plants that have borne fruit are cut away, but

United Nations

Fig. 3-5. A banana plantation in northern South
America. These workmen
are preparing to harvest a
bunch of bananas.

new plants soon arise from the underground parts. The fruits
contain a good deal of starch, some of which changes into
sugar as they ripen. They are, therefore, energy foods, and in
addition, contain vitamins A and C.

Banana raising, however, is far from being just a matter
of clearing away the jungle and setting out the plants, for
bananas are subject to insect attacks, plant diseases, and
tropical storm damage, and special handling is required to
get the fruit to the markets in good condition.

Near the close of the nineteenth century bananas began to
appear in coastal cities of the United States. This happened
at such a late date because prior to that time rapid transportation to the large markets had not been developed, and
lacking such markets, banana raisers had little reason to
produce more fruit than could be consumed locally. Once
necessary capital and management were supplied, fast-sailing
"banana boats" got into action, refrigerated cars were available at northern seaports, and effective transportation to
large markets was thus achieved. Large banana plantations

were developed in Central America, northern South America, and the West Indies, and bananas became available in every city of the United States.

Plantains are closely related to bananas, and are sometimes assigned to the species *Musa paradisiaca*. They bear fruits that are more popular with some tropical natives than are the bananas. In a recent year, for instance, almost 7 million bunches of plantains were harvested in Puerto Rico. These plantain fruits have high starch content, and therefore are cooked before they are eaten. Commonly, they are boiled, fried, or baked.

Papaya, an American Contribution. The papaya, *Carica papaya*, is another very large herb that comes from a different family of plants. Its original home was in tropical America, and records indicate that it was raised by the ancient Mayans and Incas. It can be grown from seed, and once established, a plant lives for several years.

Papaya fruits are yellow or orange in color, and weigh up to 20 pounds or more. They contain a yellow or pinkish pulp which is melon-like in taste and texture. The fruit pulp is eaten fresh, either by itself or in salads and pies, and fruit juice is obtained from it. Papaya plants are also the source of an enzyme called *papain*, which is used to tenderize meat.

Today, papaya plants are raised in southern Asia, the Philippines, on islands of the South Pacific, and in their homeland. They are not very hardy, but can be grown in the extreme southern parts of the United States.

Pineapple, Another American Favorite. The pineapple plant, *Ananas comosus*, is a perennial that belongs to the pineapple family. Apparently its homeland was northern South America, but it was carried to the West Indies and to southern Mexico in pre-Columbian times, and was raised by the ancient Incas and Aztecs.

Early explorers of the new world took pineapple plants with them on their homeward voyages, and before long, the plants were spread around the tropical and some subtropical areas of the world. They quickly became so popular that they sometimes have been raised in the greenhouses of colder countries.

Suckers are usually employed to establish new plantings of pineapples. They require a warm climate, but will survive on soils that are relatively dry. Mature plants continue to produce fruits for about ten years, but are usually replaced after the sixth year, because the fruits become smaller as the plants get older.

Pineapple fruits may weigh 20 pounds or more, and many of them are either eaten fresh or are canned. They are also, of course, the source of pineapple juice, which is now available as a fresh, quick-frozen, or canned product. In a recent year, over 15 million cases of canned pineapple had their origin in Hawaii and Puerto Rico, and another 15 million cases of pineapple juice were produced.

Unfortunately, some of the potential flavor of fresh pineapple is lost when the fruits are picked before they are ripe, which is likely to be the case if they are shipped to distant markets. We really have to visit pineapple country to discover the full possibilities of fresh pineapples.

As we have noted, bananas are the world's number one tropical fruit, but pineapples hold second place. Hawaii, the West Indies, the Philippines, the East Indies, southern Asia, and portions of Africa are locations where considerable numbers of pineapples are grown today. Hawaii, however, is the leading producer by a wide margin. Various by-products come from the pineapple canneries, and a fiber called piña is obtained from pineapple leaves.

The Oily Alligator Pear. Two species of trees belonging to the genus *Persea* of the laurel family produce vegetable-like fruits known as avocados or alligator pears. Their homeland probably extended from southern Mexico to northern South America, and avocados were well known to the Aztecs, Mayans, and Incas prior to the coming of the Spaniards.

Avocado fruits are really large, pear-shaped berries that differ from most other fruits because they contain relatively high percentages of plant oil and protein, as well as a substantial amount of carbohydrate material. As a result, tropical natives often use them as a sort of meat substitute, eating them either raw or cooked.

Soon after the Spanish conquests, avocado trees began to appear in other parts of the world. Using their fruits as ingredients of salads did not, however, become a widespread practice in the United States until the present century. The modern supply of avocado fruits comes from tropical America including the West Indies, southern Florida and California, Hawaii, islands of the South Pacific, southern Asia, and the Mediterranean area.

Bread that Grows on Trees.   A long time ago men in the East Indian region learned to raise *Artocarpus altilis,* the breadfruit tree, and in time the practice was extended to various islands of the South Pacific. The tree is a fairly large one, and it bears fruits up to eight inches in diameter. Some varieties of the fruits contain seeds, and others do not, but all of them are fruits that contain a good deal of starch and will serve as fuel foods.

Early explorers of the South Pacific area brought back tales about tropical food plants, and in 1787 Captain William Bligh set forth from England in H.M.S. *Bounty,* for the purpose of securing young breadfruit trees and conveying them to the West Indies. As everyone who has read *Mutiny on the Bounty* knows, Captain Bligh secured the trees in Tahiti, which was then known as Otaheite, but shortly thereafter a mutiny interrupted his voyage, and the mutineers took possession of the ship. So this consignment of breadfruit trees never reached the West Indies, but later on another British expedition carried out the mission successfully.

The name "breadfruit" evidently recognizes the fact that the yellow fruit pulp of this species can be dried, ground, and used to make a type of native bread. But breadfruit pulp is also eaten fresh, and the Polynesians used to bake the fruits over hot stones in earthen pits. Europeans taught them other culinary procedures, including boiling and frying.

Breadfruit trees still are important plants in their homeland, including the South Pacific, and some of them prosper in the West Indies, Central America, and northern South America. Their distribution is, of course, limited by the fact that they lack hardiness.

Mango, a Relative of the Sumacs. The mango tree is *Mangifera indica,* a member of the cashew family which also includes our familiar sumacs. This mango tree has been cultivated in the southeast Asian area for centuries; it is represented by many different varieties, and it is still a tropical species of first rank and perhaps growing importance.

The tree itself is quite large, and bears leaves throughout the year. It can be raised from seeds, but in order to preserve desired qualities, is often propagated by grafting. Fruits vary in size, some varieties being quite small and others up to several inches in length. The pulp is yellow, orange, or red in color, and is generally used as fresh fruit, although some of it is used in sauces and preserves.

Mangos were brought to the West Indies and South America in the eighteenth century. Some of them grow in Florida and California today, but their lack of hardiness prevents survival farther to the north. They are, however, grown very extensively in India, the Philippines, and portions of Africa.

Olives, Oil, and Lamps. Somewhere not far removed from Mediterranean shores, and at any rate before the time of recorded history, the olive tree, *Olea europaea,* began to assume an important role in human affairs. To be sure, its fruits were small in size, but they had one important characteristic: when they were ripe they could crushed and squeezed, and thus a substantial amount of olive oil could be obtained.

So it is not surprising that inhabitants of the ancient kingdoms around the Mediterranean Sea had olive groves that were well established in pre-Christian times. Olive oil was useful in cooking and as fuel for primitive lamps, and it also could be employed to anoint human bodies, a common custom in the early days of civilization. North American Indians used animal fats as external lubricants, but ancient Greeks and Romans relied primarily upon oil from their olives. Although times have changed and some of the old customs have been abandoned, olives and olive oil remain very important in the economy of the Mediterranean area.

If we were to pick an olive from a tree either green or

ripe, and attempt to eat it, we would experience an unpleasant surprise. The newly picked fruit would be bitter and unpalatable. Yet the olives that we buy in bottles and cans are quite tasty. This is due to the fact that when the fruits are picked they are first put through a pickling process which removes the bitter taste. Then they are washed, and later soaked in brine. Finally, they are canned or bottled for the market.

The Spaniards brought olive trees to the new world at an early date, and olive groves became established in Mexico and what is now our Southwest. Some of our canned olives and oil come from the new world sources, but we still import some pickled olives and quantities of olive oil from southern Europe.

Fruits and Nuts from Palm Trees

Various types of palm trees in tropical and semitropical areas have had an important relationship to human economy for no one knows how long. Some of them are sources of useful fruits, but other products also come from members of this group.

Dates and Desert Nomads. One species that was cultivated at a very early period in human history is the date palm, *Phoenix dactylifera*. This is a tree that grows to a height of 100 feet or more, is quite long-lived and can be propagated from both seeds and shoots. Perhaps it was first raised in or near the Fertile Crescent of southwestern Asia, and was conveyed to northern Africa not long thereafter. Centuries later, the Spaniards brought stock to Mexico, and near the end of the nineteenth century some African varieties were established in California and Arizona.

Date fruits are high in sugar content, and even contain some protein and oil; they are not only acceptable to the palate, but serve as fuel foods. The trees that produce them also have special uses in some parts of the world. Lumber and fuel come from the tree trunks, and leaves are used to fabricate baskets and crates. The terminal bud of a young tree is sometimes cut off to serve as a vegetable. Sap from the trees is used to produce an alcoholic beverage, and the fruits may be employed to provide syrup, vinegar, and alcohol.

In some desert areas, the date groves establish a way of life. They shade the desert encampment and provide it with food, utensils, and shelter. As every devotee of the cinema knows, a sheik must have his camels, tents, and desert sands. He must also have date palms if he is to appear authentic.

Date palms have one notable peculiarity. To produce fruits successfully, they must have warm, dry air about them, although at the same time, their root systems must be in contact with soil water. In moist air, the ripening fruits mold, and no crop is produced. This is the reason why date palms fare well in the vicinity of desert oases in southwestern Asia and northern Africa. Some sites in Mexico and our Southwest also provide the requisite conditions, and some of the dates we see in American markets come from this area. Others are imports from Asia and Africa.

The Coconut Palm. Another well-known member of the palm family is the coconut palm, *Cocos nucifera* (Fig. 3-6). While the date palm produces fruits, the coconut palm is the source of nuts that are enclosed in heavy husks. The coconuts you see in the markets usually have had their husks removed. When the husks are present, however, coconuts are quite capable of floating from one island to another, and this fact may account in part for their widespread distribution among islands in warmer parts of the Pacific Ocean.

It is believed that the homeland of the coconut palm may have been in the East Indies, but in the course of time men have carried this ornamental and useful tree to many tropical and subtropical lands. Coconut products, which are as many and varied as those that come from date palms, are in part derived from "wild" trees, and in part from trees on plantations. The East Indies, southern Asia, the Philippines, islands of the South Pacific and Central Pacific, and various locations in the American tropics are the main sources of these products today.

One commendable feature of the coconut palm is that it

*Australian News and
Information Bureau*

Fig. 3-6. If you live in the South Pacific and you want some coconuts, one way to get them is to climb a coconut palm.

keeps on producing its nuts throughout the year. When ripe, the partially hollow cavities within these nuts contain a liquid that is often drained off for use as a beverage. The main commercial value, however, relates to the white, fleshy "meat" that lines the coconut shell, and is a part of the plant's seed. When dried, this material is called *copra*. The "meat" can be shredded while still moist, and employed in making candies and cakes, but the coconut oil expressed from copra is the first item of commercial interest. We import a great deal of copra, and in a recent year, almost 500 million pounds of crude coconut oil were derived from this material in the United States. Coconut oil is used in manufacturing various food products, soaps, and cosmetics.

Wherever coconut trees grow, they are likely to provide many other materials that have value. When cut in half, one end of a coconut shell becomes a bowl that can be used in various ways. Or shells can be burned as fuel or converted into charcoal. Wood from the tree trunks serves as lumber and fuel, and the long leaves can be woven to fabricate many different things. Even the terminal bud of a young tree, as in the case of a date palm, may be cut off and eaten, although this means that the tree will be destroyed. To put it simply, a grove of coconut palms will provide shelter, food, and materials for building a home and making a good many items used in daily life.

Walnuts and Related Types

Pecans, hickories, butternuts, black walnuts, and English walnuts all belong to the same family of trees, which is sometimes called the walnut family. With the exception of the English walnut, which actually appears to have had its origin in southern Asia, the nut-bearing species we are interested in are native to North America, and are important not only because of the nuts they produce, but also because they are the sources of useful wood. Walnut furniture, gun stocks, and paneling are well known, and hickory handles for axes, hatchets, hammers, and other implements are as famous as hickory-smoked sausage.

The Pecan, an American Favorite. When settlers came to the new world they found the pecan tree, *Carya illinoensis*, growing wild in the southeastern part of North America, as far north and west as Indiana and Illinois, and on down into Mexico. The nuts of this species soon became popular, and it was a foregone conclusion that efforts would be made to select special varieties and establish plantings. The papershell type of pecan nut is one product of such efforts, and commercial pecan groves exist in various parts of the South and Southwest today.

In a recent year, over 45 million pounds of pecans passed through commercial outlets, and there are indications that annual production is rising steadily. Some of the nuts are marketed in their shells, and others are shelled before they enter the retail trade. Pecans serve as table nuts; they are also widely used in making ice creams, candies, and cakes.

Hickory Trees; Close Relatives of the Pecans. A number of hickory species are native to eastern North America, and all of them yield wood that is of commercial importance, although to varying degrees. Some of these hickories produce nuts that are either too small or too bitter to be of significant importance, except to squirrels and chipmunks. But the shagbark hickory (*Carya ovata*) and the bigleaf shagbark (*Carya laciniosa*) produce nuts that farmers have collected, eaten, and sometimes sold since the first days of settlement. These nuts, however, are like black walnuts and butternuts in that they have very hard shells; ordinarily, a hammer must be used to crack them.

Efforts to produce special varieties of hickory trees have had promising results, but commercial production lags far behind that of pecans, and most of the hickory nuts we see are the products of "wild" trees.

Walnuts and Butternuts. Walnuts and butternuts belong to the genus *Juglans*, the black walnut being *Juglans nigra*; the butternut or white walnut, *Juglans cinerea*; and the English walnut, *Juglans regia*.

The black walnut may be found from southern New England to Florida, and westward to Texas and Nebraska. It is a species that has been in great demand for its wood; so much so, that the nuts have been of secondary importance. Early settlers used the husks that form around the nuts to provide a dye with which to color their homespun garments.

The meat of walnuts has a high oil content, and is used to some extent in making candies and ice creams. The nut shells, however, can scarcely be cracked at the table, which explains why black walnuts are less popular than pecans, almonds, and filberts during the holiday seasons. However, they are produced in many farm woodlots, and part of the crop is sent to the markets.

Nuts from the butternut tree also have an outer husk and are elongate rather than spherical. Like walnuts, they have to be husked and cracked, and the nut meats have a high oil content. These nuts have only secondary importance, though many farmers collect and use them, and they are sold to some extent.

Butternut wood is of less strength and value than walnut wood. In times past, butternut bark was boiled in water, and the resulting brew was employed to dye fabrics, giving them a "butternut brown" appearance.

For many years, the English walnut tree has been cultivated in southern Asia and southern Europe, and more recently it has been established on our West Coast. The trees are smaller than black walnut trees, and they are much more susceptible to frost damage.

English walnuts have been a familiar sight at Christmas time for many years. Like pecans, they make good table nuts because their shells can be cracked with relative ease. In some recent years, United States production of these nuts has exceeded 100 million pounds.

The Rose Family Again

In previous discussions, attention has been drawn to the fact that the rose family has contributed many fruit-bearing species to our collection of economic plants. The story does not end here, however, because *Prunus amygdalus* is the source of the almond nuts that are such favorites both at home and abroad. The reader may recall that this genus *Prunus* also includes the peaches and plums.

Sweet and Bitter Almonds. The almond tree is another ancient favorite, which appears to have been native to the Mediterranean area or western Asia. Centuries ago it was being cultivated around the shores of the Mediterranean Sea. One variety of this species produces sweet almonds that serve as table nuts, and another variety is the source of bitter almonds. The latter are not table nuts, but are employed in the manufacture of flavoring substances. Almond trees are raised as ornamentals, as well as sources of their nuts, and many different varieties have been developed.

In more recent times, almond trees have become established

in other parts of the world, including California and nearby areas. In a recent year, home production amounted to about 145 million pounds, but we still import many almonds from old world sources. The trees are quite frost-sensitive, a fact which accounts for their limited distribution in our own country.

Nuts from the Beech Family

Many species of the beech family produce useful nuts, which include the chestnuts and the acorns. As the reader knows, acorns come from oak trees, and there are more than 80 species of oaks in the United States, some of them little more than bushy growths, and others stately forest trees.

Chestnuts and Fungus Diseases. Chestnut trees were native to Europe, eastern North America, and the Orient. The European species, of which there now are many varieties, is *Castanea sativa*. It is the main source of the chestnuts we see in markets today, and most of our present-day supply comes from southern Europe. The nuts are eaten raw, roasted, or boiled, and in Europe they often are dried, and ground into a flour which is added to some breads and soups. These nuts are more important in the European food economy than in our own.

The American chestnut is *Castanea dentata,* and until the early days of the present century it was a common and valuable tree of the eastern deciduous forests, and in some localities, the dominant species. Its nuts were smaller than those of the European chestnut, but the trees were important sources of lumber, firewood, and in the past century *tannin* used in the processing of leathers. Three other chestnut species had been brought to the United States in the nineteenth century, including the European chestnut and two smaller types: the Japanese chestnut (*Castanea crenata*) and the Chinese chestnut (*Castanea mollissima*).

Then came the chestnut blight, caused by a fungal parasite that was accidentally introduced from Asia. This fungus is *Endothia parasitica,* and it appears to have reached North

America in about 1900. It lives in the bark of chestnut and oak trees, and its attacks proved fatal to both American chestnut trees and the imported European chestnuts. Stumps of former chestnut trees still remain in the eastern forests, and from their roots, shoots continue to spring up and grow for a time. But as soon as the young trees become 10 to 20 feet high, their bark begins to crack and is promptly infected by the fatal, parasitic spores. These spores come from fungal growths in the bark of oak trees. Fortunately, the oaks are not destroyed by the attacks.

As this is written, efforts are being made to develop special varieties of American chestnut trees, or even hybrid types, which will be immune to chestnut blight, and some progress has been made. The Japanese chestnut is immune, and continues to exist in North America, but it is an inferior species insofar as lumber production is concerned.

Acorns: Foods of the Forest. Acorns, produced in abundance by many oaks, serve as food for squirrels, chipmunks, jays and certain other birds, and some members of the human species. The trouble with acorns is that they contain bitter substances including tannin. But long ago Europeans knew how to deal with this problem, and so did some American Indians. One method is to grind up the acorns, and then leach out the bitter substances. The residue can then be dried and used as a type of meal or flour.

Nuts from Various Sources

Some members of the birch family produce the nuts we call filberts and hazelnuts. Filberts are generally the larger type, and come from a number of species belonging to the genus *Corylus*, which are native to north temperate areas around the world. Some of these plants are mere shrubs, and others are substantial trees. Crossing and selection have been applied in recent years to produce varieties that yield larger nuts, and these are the ones that often appear in mixed nut assortments at Christmas time. The native American hazelnut bushes, growing in the wild, produce good but relatively small nuts. Filberts are now raised on the West Coast, and in a recent year, filbert and hazelnut production exceeded 18 million pounds.

The rather oily Brazil nut comes from trees of the genus *Bertholletia*, which grow in forests of the Amazon basin. The nuts are contained within fruits produced by these trees, as many as two dozen nuts per fruit. Inhabitants of the area gather nuts in the forests, use some as food, and convey the rest to the markets. Quantities of Brazil nuts are exported to Europe and the United States annually.

Cashew nuts come from another tropical South American tree known as *Anacardium occidentale*, which is also a good lumber tree. It is in the same plant family as the mangos and the sumacs. Unlike the Brazil nut trees, this species has been raised extensively in other parts of the world; in fact, it was well known to the ancient Incas, and early South American explorers took trees to southern Asia and to Africa in the fifteenth century. South America and India are centers of cashew nut production today, and some of these nuts also come from Florida, Mexico, the East Indies, and the Mediterranean area.

Pistachio nuts, which are sometimes called green almonds, come from a small tree (*Pistachia vera*), which perhaps was first cultivated in southwestern Asia. This tree is still a favorite in the Mediterranean area, and has been raised to some extent on our West Coast. The relatively small nuts are soaked in brine, and serve as table nuts, or are used to flavor ice creams and other foods.

A number of other nuts make greater or lesser contribution to human fare in various parts of the world. Included among them are the pinon or pine nuts, beechnuts, hicans, pilinuts, South Sea chestnuts, and a large assortment of walnuts that are produced in Central America, South America, and Asia.

4

Drugs, Chemicals, and Beverages

Looking down the dim avenue of prehistoric time, anthropologists attempt to answer many questions about man and his antecedents. As they do so, it becomes clear that they are not dealing with a recent story, for human types have existed for well over a million years. It is only during the last, small segment of this period, however, that men have been freed from a constant struggle for mere survival, and in their leisure moments, have turned to recording the events of their times.

Plants and the Healing Arts

Among the earliest records from various parts of the world, we sooner or later find some reference to the use of plants in efforts to cure diseases. Over 6000 years ago, the ancient Chinese were using drug plants, as were the Egyptians, Sumerians, and Semites long before the birth of Christ, and before there were any physicians in the modern sense of the word. On this side of the world, the Aztecs, Mayans, and Incas had all developed primitive healing arts, in which the use of plant materials figured to a greater or lesser extent. But the old records are fragmentary at best, and we cannot be sure just when and where the medicinal uses of many plants came into being.

Plant Drugs of the Greek and Roman Empires. When we move into the historical period, the record is more satisfying. A Greek named Theophrastus, who lived in the fourth century B.C., was one of the first serious students of plants. Theophrastus investigated the structure and growth of several hundred species while he tended a botanical garden in

Athens. He was followed in the first century A.D. by Discorides, a Greek who lived in Rome.

Discorides wrote a book describing the medicinal uses of plants, which was used by the physicians of Europe for centuries. In the second century A.D., Galen, another migrant Greek, became the outstanding physician of the Roman Empire. Galen's system of medicine involved the use of many plant materials, and his influence weighed heavily upon the healing arts—for better and for worse—during the ensuing 15 centuries.

Many physicians of this early period searched for drug plants in fields and forests. They also began to raise such plants in their own gardens. They observed the effects that could be produced by using various roots, stems, leaves, and fruits. Thus Discorides revealed that if 30 castor bean berries were ground up and swallowed, vomiting would result in a violent and disagreeable form. But disagreeable or not, the ancient healers clung to their plant remedies, and added new items as time went by.

Medieval Drugs.   As the Roman Empire disintegrated, Europe entered upon medieval times, which certainly were not marked by rapid advances in medical science. Germs were, of course, unknown, so Galen's followers were shadow-boxing with an unidentified group of enemies. More drugs of both plant and animal origin were added to the already imposing collection. It was not unusual to mix together 100 or more items in a single medicine, provided the sufferer seemed important enough to justify the effort.

Some of the plant drugs used at this time had genuine curative value, but others were worse than useless. The medieval drug usnea, for instance, had no curative powers, but was continued in use as late as the nineteenth century. It consisted of moss that had grown on the skull of a criminal who had been hanged in chains. Maintaining a satisfactory supply of this substance must have been something of a problem, although numerous criminals and inept politicians met their end on the gallows. Doubtless there was temptation to substitute any moss when supplies of the genuine article were running low.

In times past, there has been a close relationship between condiments, which are substances used to season foods, and the plant drugs that serve as medicines. The "spice trade" several centuries ago, which brought various condiments from India and China to Europe, was of great economic and political importance. This was not because Europeans craved more tasty food, although at the time their diets must have been most unappealing, but due to the fact that spices were thought to be useful in treating ailments. In the fifteenth century, Columbus set forth to find a shorter route to the Indies, the potential reward being domination of what was really a drug trade. Columbus failed to attain his objective, as everyone knows today, but some explorer who followed him did come upon cinchona bark in the jungles of South America.

The early European invaders of the Americas soon became familiar with tobacco, and found that at least some of the Indians who brought them supplies believed that this plant would cure various diseases. Tobacco was duly conveyed to Europe, where the practice of smoking and taking snuff gradually gained a hold, although not without considerable opposition. Any idea that tobacco was a cure-all for disease was soon dispelled.

Down to Modern Times.   The use of herbs as home remedies has by no means died out in the modern day. Many of the materials used are quite harmless and of no real virtue, and some of them actually have useful properties. Others are dangerous in the hands of inexpert people. Such people may not realize that a minute quantity of a given substance may be tolerated by the human system, but that an overdose may result in tragedy.

Modern physicians do not scour the fields and forests for drug plants, nor do they ordinarily devote much time to gardening. Many relatively useless plant substances are no longer used, for the simple reason that more effective drugs are well known and readily available. Some other plant substances have proven to be of value, but have been largely replaced by synthetic drugs that can be obtained at lower cost. But other plant materials still serve as sources of modern

U.S.D.A. photo

Fig. 4-1. The belladonna plant. This leafy herb is one source of the drug atropine.

medicines, and it is with this group that we are concerned. We continue to rely upon "wild plants" for certain drugs, but some plant species are now raised as "special crops" to insure more stable supplies. During World War I and World War II, for example, a number of drug plants were cultivated in the United States to an extent greater than is ordinarily the case.

Modern Drugs from Plants

The plant drugs that are still in common use come from many parts of the world and involve substances derived from the roots, stems, leaves, flowers, fruits, and seeds of various species. As in the past, some of the products serve both as condiments and as drugs. We shall not attempt to describe all of them, because the list is too long. We must be content with some representative examples.

The usual history of a plant drug is that herb gatherers first use the plant substance in crude form. Later, scientists isolate one or more compounds from the crude substance, and study the effects of these compounds when they are used as drugs. Still later, other scientists may learn to synthesize the useful compounds or related compounds that are even more satisfactory.

The Belladonna Plant. The plant, which bears the name *Atropa belladonna,* is a perennial that grows to a height of about three feet (Fig. 4-1). It is native to Europe and Asia, but is now raised as a special crop both abroad and in the United States. From its leaves and roots, the drug belladonna is obtained.

Belladonna contains several alkaloids, which are naturally occurring compounds of an alkaline nature. It has been used for a long time as a sedative, to reduce nasal secretion in colds and hay fever, and to treat asthma. One of its alkaloids is the drug atropine, which is highly poisonous, but has many medical uses, such as to dilate the pupil of the eye.

Atropine also occurs in leaves of the jimson weed, *Datura stramonium,* and the leaves of henbane (see page 102). The drug has been synthesized.

Capsicum Peppers. The capsicum peppers are plants of the American tropics, which were in common use when the first European explorers reached the shores of the new world. Subsequently, they have been raised in various lands, and represent a case in which the plant products serve as both condiments and medicines.

These peppers belong to the genus *Capsicum,* and include such types as the sweet peppers that we commonly see in salads. But they also include the pimentos, tabascos, and chilies. Red or cayenne pepper is made from the dried and powdered fruits of chili peppers. These same chilies are the source of the drug capsicum, which is still used to some extent as a stimulant and counter-irritant.

A Laxative from Trees. We do not ordinarily think of a laxative as growing on trees, yet cascara comes from the rather bitter bark of a small tree called the western buckthorn, *Rhamnus purshiana,* native to California and the Pacific Northwest. Most of the bark used to make the product still comes from "wild" trees, although recently some attempts have been made to raise buckthorns in plantings.

When Spanish settlers came to the West Coast many years ago, they found the native Indians using dried buckthorn bark because of its laxative properties. The Spaniards followed suit, and named the laxative substance *cascara sagrada,* implying that it was "sacred bark."

Coca Plants and Cocaine. The coca plant, *Erythroxylon coca,* is a bush-like species native to South America. Its leaves contain cocaine and several other alkaloids (Fig. 4-2). The ancient Incas and their Indian successors were well aware of the coca plant, and made a practice of chewing its leaves. This enabled them to resist hunger and fatigue, as well as pain associated with various ailments. Coca chewing, however, is habit forming, and may eventually lead to death. Just the same, the habit of chewing coca leaves remains common in South America today, as well as in the Orient where it has been adopted by many of the inhabitants.

The coca plant is now raised both in South America and the East Indies. Bushes bear usable leaves in about four years, and these may be picked from time to time without destroying the plants. Cocaine is extracted from these leaves and is used as a local anesthetic and for other medical purposes. Taken by way of the mouth, small doses stimulate and then depress the central nervous system. Like the chewing of coca leaves, the use of cocaine can be habit forming.

An African Stimulant. Apparently natives of tropical Africa have chewed cola (or kola) nuts for centuries, using them as a sort of home remedy that stimulates and wards off fatigue. This practice, unlike that of chewing coca leaves, is not damaging to the system unless carried to excess, and is not habit forming.

The nuts come from *Cola nitida,* a West African tree that

is now cultivated in its homeland, in the West Indies, and in tropical areas of South America and Asia. The nuts contain caffeine, a familiar drug also found in coffee and tea, and also another drug called kolanin.

While many African natives still find satisfaction in chewing the nuts, other markets have been found for them. They are the source of cola, an extract that is used in the production of the popular cola beverages.

A Drug to Produce Mutations. A number of plants native to the shores of the Mediterranean Sea are known as meadow saffrons. One of them is *Colchicum autumnale,* a perennial that grows up each year from underground parts. Its corms and seeds contain the poisonous alkaloid called *colchicine,*

W. H. Hodge

Fig. 4-2. Leaves and fruits of the coca plant.

which has been used in various biological experiments designed to produce mutations, or new, inheritable characters. Colchicine also has a medical use, inasmuch as it is employed in carefully regulated doses to relieve attacks of gout.

From Poisoned Arrows to Shock Therapy. Now and then some substance known to primitive tribesmen turns out to have quite useful properties. A fairly recent example is provided by *curare,* which South American Indians have used to poison arrow heads for many years. Various tribesmen prepare different types of curare, and they are usually reluctant to reveal how it is done.

In general, however, roots, stems, and bark of woody plants such as *Strychnos toxifera* and related species are boiled and then processed to yield a poisonous paste that can be applied to the points of weapons. When curare enters an animal's body, a spreading paralysis results, and ends with a heart failure.

This effect seems to be due to several alkaloids, one of them being curarine. A standard product of curarine has now been developed for medical use; it is a strong sedative, and is sometimes employed in operations to relax muscles. It is also used in the shock therapy given in treatment of some types of mental disorders.

An Old Chinese Favorite. Several species of the genus *Ephedra* are native to Asia, and have been used by the Chinese as a drug source for thousands of years. Ephedra plants are shrubs that have no leaves, and look somewhat like our familiar horsetails. Unfortunately, crude drug substances obtained from them can be dangerous when used as home remedies.

In recent times, the standard drug ephedrine has been developed, and is used in the treatment of asthma, hay fever, and colds, as a stimulator of the circulation, and to counteract overdoses of depressants. But ephedra plants have lost their one-time importance, because a method of synthesizing ephedrine was discovered in 1923, and most of the commercial drug now comes from this source.

Ergot from a Fungus. It is not only from herbs and trees

that we get useful drugs, and ergot may be used as an example of this fact. The history of this substance is unusual, going back to the disease "St. Anthony's fire" of medieval times. This dreaded affliction is now known as the disease ergotism, caused by eating rye bread made from grain blighted by the fungus *Claviceps purpurea.*

This fungus lives as a parasite on wheat, barley, and other plants of the grass family. The fungus grows on a young seed, and in time replaces it with a fungal fruiting body which is more or less black in color. The cause of the disease was discovered in 1597, but the news spread slowly, and epidemics of ergotism continued until the end of the past century. Even today, people pressed by hunger are likely to "take a chance," and eat the blighted grain.

Eventually, the drug known as ergot was extracted from the fungal fruiting bodies. It was found to contain several alkaloids, and to be particularly useful in controlling hemorrhages of the uterus. Prior to World War II, we imported most of the ergot grain used in drug manufacture from Europe and Asia, but today much of it comes from North American sources. This is one case in which spoiled grain has a special usefulness.

The Foxglove—an Ornamental Drug Plant. Most of the plants that give rise to useful drugs would scarcely be raised as flower sources, but the foxglove (*Digitalis purpurea*) is an exception. This plant originally came from Europe, but now grows wild in portions of both North and South America. It is also a drug plant that is cultivated in the United States, being raised from seeds. Foxglove is a biennial, growing to a height of about four feet.

The very useful drug digitalis is extracted from the leaves of foxglove. For this purpose, leaves are picked from both first- and second-year plants. The drug is used in various tonics, and to increase the secretion of urine. But it is most important because it stimulates heart action, and is often employed in the treatment of circulatory diseases.

Ginseng for the Orientals. We now come to the unusual case of a substance that has not been demonstrated to have

any important curative powers, but nevertheless is used extensively in China to treat a variety of diseases. This is the root
of the ginseng plant, and the original source was the Oriental
species *Panax schinseng*. But Oriental supplies began to run
low, and American ginseng, *Panax quinquefolius*, was also
pressed into service. The latter plant was once common enough
in the forested areas of eastern North America, but herb
gatherers have greatly depleted the natural supply.

As a consequence, a budding industry devoted to the raising of ginseng has developed in our own country. The plants
can be produced from seeds, and about six years' growth is
required for best results. Then the roots are dug up, cleaned,
dried, and sent to the market.

Another Source of Atropine and Related Drugs.   The henbane plant is *Hyoscyamus niger*, which sometimes grows as
an annual, but otherwise as a biennial. Apparently it is
native to Europe and Asia, but it is now found in other parts
of the world, including North America. We import most of
our henbane, but in time of war it has been raised as a
special crop.

The leaves of henbane contain several poisonous alkaloids,
including hyoscyamine, which has some of the same effects
as atropine, and is used as a sedative and to relieve pain.
Another alkaloid in henbane is scopolamine, which serves to
produce so-called twilight sleep; scopolamine is also found in
the leaves of jimson weed (*Datura stramonium*). A third alkaloid from henbane is atropine, as noted on page 97 and henbane appears to be the best natural source of this drug.

Ipecac from South America.   A shrub-like South American
plant called *Cephaelis ipecacuanha* is a source of the drug
ipecac, which was in very common use a generation ago. The
drug substance comes from the dried roots of the plant. It
has been used to induce vomiting, to treat amebic dysentery
victims, and also as an ingredient of cough medicines.

Ipecac contains the alkaloids emetine and cephaeline. Pure
emetine is now available, and has largely replaced ipecac in
the treatment of amebic dysentery.

Fruit of the Poppy.   Several varieties of the poppy plant,

Papaver somniferum, are the sources of opium, a narcotic which was known to the ancients, and whose use became almost world-wide at an early date. There are still a great many opium smokers and opium eaters in Asia, and the opium poppy is a common crop plant in Egypt, India, and China.

A juice that comes from the poppy capsules is the source of the drug. Unfortunately, the practices of eating and smoking opium soon produce addicts, who are likely to become victims of delerium and death in due course. An overdose of opium is fatal because the respiratory processes fail.

Among others, opium contains the alkaloids morphine and codeine. Morphine is well known as a pain reliever and depressant, and has found a use in the treatment of many human ills. There is always, however, the lurking danger that the morphine habit will be formed. Like morphine, codeine has been used extensively as a sedative, and to reduce muscular spasms. Heroin is derived from morphine, is habit-forming, and is the favorite of drug addicts in the United States.

Fleaworts and Laxatives. Three species of fleaworts belonging to the genus *Plantago* are annual plants which appear to have been native to southern Asia and Europe. They are now cultivated in the old world, and have appeared as "wild" plants in other lands.

These fleaworts are the source of psyllium seeds, which are used to produce a mild laxative action. In the human intestine, the seeds absorb water and swell; hence, the wastes tend to become more bulky and to remain soft. Extracts from psyllium seeds also find a use in certain manufacturing processes.

Cinchona and Quinine. From old records, we are reasonably sure that malaria was a common affliction in ancient Rome and medieval Europe. Over on the other side of the world, South American Indians evidently had learned to relieve malarial fevers by chewing the bark of cinchona trees. In the Andean region, there are about a dozen species of trees belonging to the genus *Cinchona,* and the bark of some of these species contains useful amounts of quinine.

Various tales have been told as to how European explorers discovered cinchona bark and brought it back to Europe early in the seventeenth century, but we do not know just when and how this event occurred. We do know that the Jesuits were distributing powdered cinchona bark in Europe after about 1632, and that "Jesuits powder" began to be accepted when it was used to cure a malarial attack of King Louis XIV of France. It was not until 1820, however, that quinine was isolated from the bark.

Meanwhile, natural stands of cinchona trees began to become depleted in the Andean country; and in 1854, Dutch planters initiated experiments with cinchona trees in the East Indies, and the British soon followed suit in India and Ceylon. As we have noted, not all types of cinchona trees produce quinine in notable quantity, so the early years were spent developing plantings that were truly productive. In Java, the results were good, and after a time the less successful plantings on the Asiatic mainland were abandoned. Thereafter, the Dutch had more or less of a monopoly until World War II, when we once more turned to the forests of South America for a quinine supply.

One method of harvesting cinchona bark is simply to cut the trees and strip the bark from the trunks and larger branches (Fig. 4-3). New trees will often grow up from the stumps that are left. The bark is shipped to drug manufacturers who extract the quinine.

Quinine is still in demand, but it is no longer the only antimalarial drug. As World War II began, an antimalarial drug called atabrine was synthesized, to be followed after the war by drugs such as chloroquine, paludrine, and pentaquine.

A Mixture of Drugs and Perfumes. The case of sandalwood is interesting, because this product is the source of lumber used to make chests and boxes, as well as the source of an oil that goes into perfumes and Oriental medicines. These materials are obtained from *Santalum album*, and several related species which are native to the East Indies and southern Asia. They have been in use for a very long time, and natural supplies of the trees have been greatly reduced.

Some of the trees, however, are now cultivated in other lands. The oil for perfumes and medicines is obtained by distilling wood chips.

Sassafras Trees and Spring Tonic. The sassafras tree, *Sassafras albidum,* is widely distributed over eastern North America, and is well known for the fact that it bears leaves of variable shape. The Indians used sassafras root bark, and early colonists soon learned to brew a spring tonic from this material, as well as a sassafras tea. Whatever their virtues may or may not have been, both the tonic and tea have lost favor in these modern times.

Sassafras root bark, however, remains in demand, because it is used to flavor soft drinks and various other substances. The supply comes from natural growths of trees in forests and woodlots.

Ewing Galloway

Fig. 4-3. Cutting a cinchona tree in a South American jungle. The bark of cinchona trees is the source of the drug quinine.

Nux Vomica and Strychnine. Nux vomica comes from seeds that develop in the large fruits of *Strychnos nux-vomica,* a tree that is native to southern Asia, the Philippines, and Australia. It is an alkaloid poison, and an overdose produces stiffness in the neck, labored breathing, convulsions, and death. But minute doses can be used in tonics and stimulants. Strychnine is derived from nux vomica, and is sometimes used to treat nervous disorders and paralysis.

Other Drugs from Plants. Many other drugs have been, and in some cases continue to be obtained from various higher plants. Among those not previously mentioned are aconite from the roots of the monkshood plant, aloes from leaves of aloe plants, angelica from fruits of the angelica plant, caraway from seeds of the caraway plant, castor oil from beans of the castor bean plant, coriander from coriander fruits, eucalyptus from leaves of the blue gum tree, gentian from roots of *Gentiana lutea,* goldenseal from roots of the goldenseal plant, hamamel from the witch hazel bush, jalap from the roots of *Exogonium purga,* licorice from the roots of *Glycyrrhiza globra,* lobelia from the leaves of Indian tobacco, podophyllum from the roots of the may apple, quassia from the wood of quassia trees, rhubarb from roots of an Asiatic rhubarb plant, santonin from flowers of the Levant wormseed plant, senega root from the senega snakeroot plant, senna from leaves of cassia plants, slippery elm from bark of the red elm tree, squills from the bulbs of *Urginea maritima,* and valerian from roots of the garden heliotrope.

The Antibiotics

By definition, an *antibiotic* is a substance produced by one microorganism that will kill another microorganism. So without question, antibiotics have existed in natural form since remote times, but it is only recently that we have become truly aware of their usefulness, and have added them to the array of modern "miracle drugs."

On the Trail of Something New. It is probably fair to say that the study of antibiotics originated with the French chemist Louis Pasteur. In the latter part of the past century, Pasteur noted that a certain bacterium appeared to be antagonistic to the germs of anthrax. Other cases of similar antagonisms were soon observed by several European scientists. In 1896, a substance called mycophenolic acid was extracted from a mold of the genus *Penicillium,* and was used experimentally to kill anthrax germs.

Just before the dawn of the twentieth century, two German doctors developed a microbial extract which was used to treat various diseases. It was called pyrocyanase, and had the fates decreed otherwise, a search for other antibiotics might have developed then and there. But apparently pyrocyanase, although popular for a time, fell into disuse before many years had passed.

This left the way open for Sir Alexander Fleming to make a discovery which finally triggered the interest of the scientific world. This happened in 1928 when Fleming observed that bacteria on one of his culture plates were being dissolved adjacent to a colony of *Penicillium* mold. Fleming realized that a substance from the mold, which he called penicillin, was responsible, and published his findings in 1929. Meanwhile, Fleming continued to use modest amounts of penicillin available to him in other experiments. So Fleming's discovery remained largely dormant for the time being.

In the mid-thirties, prontosil, the first of the sulfa drugs, made its appearance, to be followed shortly thereafter by sulfapyridine, sulfadiazene, and others. For a time there was hope that the developing battery of sulfa drugs would provide effective controls for any and all germ diseases; but of course this did not prove to be the case, although sulfa drugs have been very important factors in recent medical advances. They are synthetic drugs which were developed from coal tar dyes.

During this third decade, Renee Dubos of the Rockefeller Institute for Medical Research discovered gramicidin, a substance produced by a soil bacterium, which was an effective inhibitor of gram-positive cocci, and reported his findings in 1939.

In 1939, Europe had once more been plunged into armed conflict, and in the aftermath of battles, germ-killing drugs were in high demand. At Oxford University, H. W. Florey, E. B. Chain, N. G. Heatley, and a group of co-workers took up the penicillin trail again. One of the early problems was to develop a method of producing penicillin in quantity. American drug firms joined in the quest, a more productive *Penicillium* mold was found growing on a muskmelon in Illinois, and the wheels soon began to turn with gratifying results. Many hospitals had penicillin in 1944, and it became generally available in 1945. Today, there are several types of penicillins derived from molds.

Since the mid-forties, the capabilities of penicillin have been tested rather extensively. It has proved effective against a variety of bacteria of the spherical or coccus type, against a number of spirochaetes including the syphilis organism, against the ray fungus, and against the bacillus of anthrax. It is sometimes used to prevent, as well as to cure infections.

Streptomycin and Soil Screening. The development of streptomycin by Dr. S. A. Waksman and his associates at Rutgers University was announced in 1944. The drug was derived from another mold named *Streptomyces griseus.* Waksman had been searching for such a substance for a number of years, and had obtained and tested a large number of mold extracts. Streptomycin proved to be effective against all of the organisms that are penicillin-sensitive, although not equally effective in the case of the cocci. In addition, it could combat germs in the gram-negative group, such as the organisms of bubonic plague, tuberculosis, and tularemia.

One corollary outcome of the streptomycin discovery was the demonstration that a soil-screening program could yield practical results. *Streptomyces* came from the soil, so why not other useful molds? A number of drug firms were intrigued by this possibility and went to work on the problem with results that were soon evident.

The Discovery of Chloromycetin. A new antibiotic named chloromycetin was announced in 1947. Dr. P. R. Burkholder of Yale, working with Parke-Davis scientists, obtained it from

Streptomyces venezuelae. This *Streptomyces* was one of several thousand foreign types that were screened, and as the name indicates, it came from Venezuela. Shortly thereafter, the new drug was synthesized, so it was no longer necessary to extract it from the mold.

Chloromycetin proved to be a welcome addition to the growing list of chemical defenses, because it gave good results against the typhoid bacillus, and the various rickettsias that cause the typhus fevers. It has also proved useful in combatting tularemia and certain infections of the excretory system. It is a drug that can be taken by way of the mouth.

Aureomycin and Terramycin. Soil screening continued, and so did the development of new antibiotics. At the Lederle Laboratories, Dr. B. M. Duggar obtained a gold-colored extract from *Streptomyces aureofaciens,* which was named aureomycin and could also be administered orally. In this case, the mold came from a soil sample obtained in Illinois, and was a species new to science. Aureomycin soon proved to be a wide-spectrum type of antibiotic, which means that it was effective against a large number of microparasites. It defends against all germs that are penicillin-sensitive, and some others, such as the organisms of the typhus fevers and tularemia.

Meanwhile, scientists at the Pfizer Laboratories extracted terramycin from *Streptomyces rimosus.* Terramycin proved to be another wide-spectrum antibiotic, effective against substantially the same germs that are aureo-sensitive.

Toxic Effects and Resistant Strains. Various new antibiotics have made their appearance since the advent of terramycin in 1950. About two dozen antibiotics are in common use, some of them employed largely in the treatment of skin infections, rather than as internal medicines. As in the case of other drugs, quantities of antibiotics are in demand, not alone for the treatment of ailing humans, but also for the protection of domesticated animals.

In part, the production of new drugs represents the result of competition among drug manufacturers. But there are sound, scientific reasons why new drug substances need to be developed today and in the foreseeable future. One of them is that in the human population there are always a few individuals who may prove to be sensitive to an otherwise safe drug. Or there are individuals who *become* sensitive to the drug. So the existence of alternate defenses makes it possible to select a drug which will not evoke an unfavorable reaction. To put it another way, the drug which is non-toxic to the vast majority of people may prove toxic to a few individuals.

Another incentive for continued research is the fact that microparasites have an exasperating way of developing *immune strains.* Apparently what happens is about as follows. In every germ population, there is individual variation, just as there is in any other kind of population. Suppose that 10 million germs of species A are brought in contact with drug X. Drug X kills all but a half dozen of the germs. The half dozen survive because, by chance, they happen to be immune to drug X. Having survived, they proceed to grow and reproduce. Their descendants are also X-immune. When these descendants become numerous enough in the species A population, drug X is likely to lose much of its one-time potency. Now we need a new drug—drug Y—to which the immune strain of species A is sensitive.

Finally, there is the pleasing prospect of a new drug which may be less toxic than some of its predecessors, or of a new product which is effective against some group of microparasites that so far is not well controlled. Present defenses against a large number of bacteria are reasonably good. But defenses against some other bacteria and certain viruses and parasitic fungi leave much to be desired.

Many of the antibiotics we now use come from the mold type of fungus, and others from bacteria. In either case, of course, they are of plant origin. A few, such as chloromycetin and prostaphlin are synthesized, but in other cases we must still rely upon plants for their production.

Other Products from Molds. We use a surprising amount of citric acid each year in medicines, soft drinks, foods, candies, and various manufacturing processes. Most of this citric acid is obtained by mold fermentation, as is another industrial product known as gluconic acid. In addition, various useful enzymes are produced by growing molds or bacteria on grain or in laboratory cultures.

Starches, Sugars, and Alcohols

Green plants manufacture sugars and often convert them into starch for storage purposes. But some green plants build up food reserves in the form of sugars, or at least have considerable amounts of sugars in their saps and growing tissues. It is from such plants that we obtain the vast quantities of commercial sugar that the human population consumes each year.

Sugar from Cane Plants. Centuries ago, some enterprising natives of southeastern Asia or perhaps the East Indies evidently began to cultivate a wild grass plant, which ultimately was to become our sugar cane, *Saccharum officinarum*. This plant is a perennial which grows to a height of ten feet or more, and thrives in a tropical or semitropical area where there is abundant rainfall. Sugar cane was brought to the Americas in the sixteenth century. Although we usually think of this species as one that provides sugar, it is actually the source of various products, including alcohol, cattle food, molasses, paper, rum, and wallboard.

Sugar cane plants are raised from cuttings, and their stems are usually harvested just after the plants have been in flower. At a mill, the stems are chopped up, and the plant juices are squeezed out between rollers. The remaining solid materials are used to make wallboard and paper, and they are also mixed with molasses to form a food for cattle.

The raw juices that have been expressed from the cane stalks are processed to get rid of materials other than sugars, and then boiled down until much of the sugar forms crystals. The liquid portion is now drained off as molasses, and a brown sugar remains. This brown sugar is further processed and purified to obtain the white sugar of commerce. Powdered sugar is a mixture of finely ground white sugar and starch.

Sugar from Beets. The sugar beet (*Beta vulgaris*) is a

Sugar Information

Fig. 4-4. Stalks of sugar cane ready for the mill. Sugar cane is raised in many warm countries.

possible descendant of the wild European species *Beta maritima*. The story of its rise to fame begins in 1747, when a German scientist named Marggraf crystallized sugar from the juices of several beets. But in the beets of Marggraf's day, sugar was not present in large amounts.

A more sugary type of beet was clearly required, and another scientist developed a beet variety known as the white Silesian. This scientist was Achard, who also worked out a process for extracing sucrose from the beets. For the time being, little came of Achard's efforts, but in 1811 politics took a hand in the proceedings. Napoleon began to subsidize sugar beet factories so that France could avoid trading with England, and the French joined the Germans in the beet-raising enterprise. Mass selection was used in an effort to improve yields, and a superior beet type known as the imperial resulted. In the middle of the nineteenth century, the production of sugar from beets began to be an important European industry.

Meanwhile, sugar beet seed had been brought to North America, and various attempts were made to raise the plants and operate sugar beet factories. For fifty years these attempts were largely unsuccessful, but toward the close of the nineteenth century, the results began to show promise; and after World War I beet sugar production became well established. By this time, the methods of Mendelian selection were known, and special varieties of beets that resist beet diseases common in the American environment were developed. The modern sugar beet is very different from the plants Marggraf experimented with a century ago.

The sugar beet is a biennial that is planted in rows and harvested in the fall. It can be raised in areas too cold for sugar cane, including irrigated tracts in our own West. At harvest time, the beets are hauled to beet factories, cut into strips, and then heated in flowing water to remove the sugar. The resulting fluid is then processed, and the sugar is crystallized out of solution. Chemically, the product is the same as the white sugar obtained from sugar cane.

In this case also, several by-products result. Beet tops and beet pulp are used as animal foods and in fertilizers. The equivalent of molasses goes into animal foods, or is used as a source of alcohol. In a recent year, world production of cane sugar was about 32 million tons, and production of beet sugar about 24 million tons.

Sugar from Trees. The sugar maple, *Acer saccharum,* is native to the northeastern part of our country, and was used by Indians as a source of sugar long before the first settlers arrived. Trees of this species, and sometimes related maples, are tapped early in the spring, and sap is collected from them (Fig. 4-5). Some of the water in the sap is then removed by evaporation, leaving the maple syrup of commerce. Various methods are employed to crystallize maple sugar out of the syrup.

Certain species of tropical palms produce saps that contain large amounts of sugar. These trees are also a source of syrup, and of a crude sugar that is sold in some world markets. As a matter of fact, various species of trees, including some

Standard Oil Co., N.J.
Fig. 4-5. In early spring, holes are drilled in the trunks of hard maple trees so that the sugary sap can flow through a small tube and collect in a bucket.

fast-growing types, have saps that contain a good deal of sugar, and in northern Europe a process for the extraction of this sugar has been developed.

Syrups from Sorghums.   Some of the sorghums, which were discussed on page 30, are known as sweet sorghums because they contain relatively large amounts of sugar. They are useful forage plants, but also serve as sources of syrups. Of African and Asiatic origins, various types are now grown in the United States, and in a recent year sorgo syrup production amounted to 2 million gallons.

Starch for Food and for Industry.   Starch is used in foods, in the manufacture of sugar and commercial alcohol, in laundering, and in garment manufacturing. It can be treated with nitric acid to form nitrostarch, which is an explosive sometimes used in weapons such as hand grenades.

Most of the starch consumed in the United States comes from corn, although the oldest source probably was wheat, and Europeans depend upon potatoes for most of their supply. Starch is also extracted from rice and the stems or roots of certain tropical plants.

Industrial Alcohol. Industrial alcohol can be made from a variety of plant materials. In this country, however, most of it comes directly or indirectly from corn and potatoes. Yeasts carry on the process of fermentation, and when this is completed ethyl alcohol is obtained by distilling the "mash." Substances that denature the alcohol so that it cannot be used as a beverage are now added.

Methyl alcohol, or wood alcohol, is a poisonous type that is made by distilling wood. Both ethyl and methyl alcohol have many uses in industry, such as in the manufacture of paints and varnishes. Denatured ethyl alcohol has also been used extensively as an anti-freeze compound. In a recent year, over 500 million gallons of denatured alcohol were produced to meet the demands of industry.

Plant Beverages

Everyone knows that a number of beverages in common use come from plants. We are accustomed to our fruit and vegetable juices, including those obtained from tomatoes, carrots, oranges, grapefruits, lemons, limes, and pineapples, and are aware that they contain useful vitamins. We are not so well acquainted with certain plant beverages used in other parts of the world.

Yerba maté, for example, is made from the leaves of small, South American trees belonging to the genus *Ilex*. These trees are raised from seed, and were prized by South American Indians long before any Europeans reached that continent. But the newcomers from the old world also approved of maté, which has remained a popular beverage. The native Indians had depended upon natural supplies, but the Jesuits began to raise *Ilex* plants, which are shrub-like when cultivated.

Hot water is poured over dried *Ilex* leaves to produce the beverage, which varies from green to brown in color. Maté contains the stimulant caffeine, but in smaller quantity than it is found in tea or coffee. For some reason not known to the writer, maté has never become especially popular in the United States.

Another "tea" that has never achieved world-wide acceptance is kat (also khat, Arabian tea, and African tea), which is made from leaves of *Catha edulis,* a north African shrub that the Arabs were raising, perhaps even before they had discovered coffee. Kat also is a relatively mild stimulant.

Coffee from Africa.   Coffee comes from three African trees belonging to the genus *Coffea.* The most important of these is *Coffea arabica,* an Abyssinian species. Except among the Arabs, coffee drinking apparently got off to a slow start, although in the sixteenth century the Turks had adopted the practice from the Arabs, and Italians were experimenting with a few coffee trees. But coffee drinking hardly qualified as a European custom until the eighteenth century. Then the Dutch began to plant coffee trees in the East Indies, and the French introduced coffee in the West Indies and thereafter in South America. Coffee trees require a tropical climate, a rich soil, and plenty of moisture. The young plants must be cultivated and partially shaded.

During the eighteenth century, a good many Europeans believed that coffee drinking was outlandish, evil, and perhaps downright dangerous, inasmuch as some claimed that the beverage was intoxicating. Other Europeans evidently regarded the drink as a welcome stimulant, and some even thought it might be a drug as useful as cinchona bark. In fact, one seventeenth century idea held that coffee would cure victims of gout and scurvy. Of course, this hope proved to be vain, but it illustrates the fact that people were on the lookout for effective drugs 300 years ago, even as they are today.

Coffee "beans" are seeds that develop within fleshy fruits. These seeds contain the stimulant drug caffeine. When a

Pan American Coffee Bureau

Fig. 4-6. South American workers spreading coffee beans so that they will be dried by the sun's rays.

coffee fruit is harvested, the fleshy materials are removed by one process or another, which leaves a pair of seeds within a parchment covering. The parchment is now disposed of, and later, the coffee beans are roasted and often ground. Portions of different coffees are blended to yield products of rather distinctive flavors. Sometimes chickory root is added to the products, especially for the benefit of Europeans. In recent years, many coffee extracts have been marketed. Most of the world's coffee supply now comes from tropical America.

The Old Asian Favorite. The tea plant is *Camellia sinensis,* and its leaves also contain the stimulant caffeine. This plant is native to the southeast Asian area, where the habit of tea drinking became established centuries ago. Europeans began to drink tea in the sixteenth century, and ultimately the practice became world-wide, with the English ensconced in first place as the champion tea consumers.

Many different varieties of the tea shrub have been developed under cultivation. Tea growers generally keep the plants cut back to a height of no more than five feet. Like coffee trees, the plants are perennials, which grow best in tropical and subtropical areas where they may even thrive on relatively poor soil.

Green tea consists of leaves that have been dried and rolled. Black teas are produced by fermenting the rolled leaves, and then drying them. Various teas are blended, and some are scented by drying flowers with the tea leaves. China, India, Ceylon, and Japan are the leading tea producers, but some tea is grown in other parts of the world, including South America and Africa.

Chocolate and Chocolate Candies. These substances owe their existence to the fruits of a small, tropical American tree, *Theobroma cacao,* which was cultivated by the natives of Central and South America centuries ago. The Aztecs and Mayans were familiar with the plant, and even used cocoa beans as a sort of money.

The drink known as chocolate reached Europe in the sixteenth century, and in time became popular in many parts of the world. Today, cacao trees are largely raised in Africa, South America, Central America, the West Indies, and the East Indies.

Cacao trees require a warm climate, rich soil, plenty of moisture, and partial shading. Their fruits are pod-like structures as much as a foot in length, each of them containing from 24 to 50 beans or seeds. In harvesting, the pods are split open, and masses of the beans are then fermented. The beans with their shell-like coverings are now dried, polished, and roasted. Next, the shells are removed, and the fleshy seeds are ground to form a chocolate paste. Sugar, sometimes milk, and various flavors are added to the chocolate paste to make chocolate candies. Cocoa for beverages is produced by removing oils from the chocolate paste, and then powdering the dried residue.

The shells of cocoa beans usually go into livestock foods, but the fats become the cocoa butter that is used in candies, drugs, and cosmetics. So the cacao tree is not only the source of a popular beverage, but of foods as well.

5

Fibers, Oils, Tobacco, and Rubber

Mr. and Mrs. John Stonehatchet, early Europeans of the postglacial period, probably were accustomed to fashioning their garments from animal hides; but before the stone age ended, prehistoric Europeans were employing flax fibers to produce fabrics and other materials of their developing economy.

Today, we obtain fibers from a number of plants that we raise as crops, and also from a variety of forest trees. Some of these fibers are stiff, some are pliable, some are long, some are short, some are coarse, and others are fine; in fact, nature provides many different kinds of fibers which will satisfy all sorts of needs.

Similarly, we extract oils from numerous plant substances, as well as other materials used in making plastics and adhesives. The range of products that emerge from factories that use plant substances as raw materials is startling to anyone who has not had first-hand experience with the miracles of modern technology. Plant substances that were considered factory refuse only a few years ago are now utilized to produce all sorts of useful items. We cannot hope to deal with all such products in this book, and must be content to discuss a few representative examples.

The Fiber Crops

Various types of plant fibers are modern sources of paper, fabrics, rope, twine, packing and upholstering materials, and in the case of large, coarse strands, woven articles such as hats and baskets. Of course we also use a number of animal fibers and an ever-expanding group of synthetic or plastic fibers. Incidentally, plastics come from inorganic materials in some cases, from organic materials such as plant substances in others, and also from mixtures of organic and inorganic substances.

King Cotton. One of the old and time-honored sources of plant fibers are cotton plants belonging to the genus *Glossypium* of the mallow family. Some of these cotton plants were native to the old world, where they were pressed into service long ago, but others originated in tropical and semitropical America, where their products were utilized by men of the pre-Columbian period. In fact, the use of cotton in America may antedate a similar development in the old world.

So the cotton plants that are raised today have multiple origins. The fibers that come from them represent seed hairs, which vary in size and form among the many varieties of cotton that now exist.

There are about 40 species of cotton, which grow as woody shrubs or small trees. But most of the varieties grown today are derived from four species. The species commonly raised in many parts of the world, and the outstanding favorite in this country, is American upland cotton, *Glossypium hirsutum*. We also raise some so-called Egyptian cotton (*Glossypium barbadense*), which is another native of the new world. Cotton plants thrive in tropical and semitropical areas, where there is abundant sunshine and soil moisture. They are generally perennials when left to their own devices, but are usually grown as annuals under cultivation.

Each seed hair or fiber of a cotton plant is developed from a cell in the seed coat. Some of these fibers are short and fuzzy, and are called "linters." Others are from a half inch to almost two inches long; they are the "staples" that are used to make fabrics. The length of the staples depends upon the variety of cotton and the conditions under which the cotton is grown. A cotton staple tends to twist when it dries out, and this quality makes it possible to spin thread or yarn with comparative ease. Preferred staples are long and slender, but for some purposes, two or more varieties of staples may be blended.

Fig. 5-1.   Workers harvesting cotton in a Texas field.

Natives of India learned to twist cotton fibers into yarn and weave fabrics by hand centuries before the Christian Era, and India remained dominant in cotton goods production until the end of medieval times. Then the manufacture of cotton fabrics became important in southern Europe, and later in England. A series of eighteenth century inventions gave impetus to the cotton industry, and included machines for spinning and weaving, as well as Eli Whitney's cotton gin which stripped fibers from the seeds. This represented an early phase of the continuing tendency to devise machines that could do the job faster and at less cost than it could be done by hand. Before Whitney's time, the separation of seeds from cotton fiber had been a very time-consuming process; a man might work for two or three years before he had separated enough clean cotton fiber to make a single bale.

Cotton production got underway in our own South during

the colonial period, but at first yields were small, and they were largely processed in farm homes. The advent of the cotton gin in 1793 marked the turning point in the cotton industry, and before long American production of cotton began to expand. Soon after the Revolutionary War, at least one American power weaving mill began to turn out cotton fabric. However, there was more than enough cotton to supply local demands. So as the years passed, increasing quantities of baled cotton were shipped to the English mills.

When the War Between the States began, the English cotton fabric industry was virtually dependent upon supplies of American cotton, and such supplies were largely cut off by the wartime blockade. As a result, men in Asia, North Africa, and South America took up cotton raising to satisfy the world demand, and American cotton was never again in the favorable competitive position it once enjoyed. In a recent year, world production of cotton was about 12 million tons, of which about 3½ million tons came from the United States. Other major producers were China with over 2½ million tons, Soviet Russia with nearly 2 million tons, India with about 900 thousand tons, Brazil with nearly 700 thousand tons, Mexico with about 500 thousand tons, Pakistan with 360 thousand tons, and Egypt with 330 thousand tons. These figures are in short tons (2000 pounds), and since a bale of cotton weighs 500 pounds, the number of bales may be easily calculated.

Cotton yarn is used to produce a wide variety of fabrics. Some cotton fabrics commonly employed in making garments are batiste, broadcloth, calico, cambric, chenille, cotton flannel and flannelette, corduroy, covert, denim, duck, gingham, lawn, organdy, percale, and poplin. There are also other cotton fabrics such as awning cloth, beach cloth, cheesecloth, cord for tires, damask, muslin, and ticking.

In 1844, John Mercer, an Englishman, developed a method of treating cotton fibers with caustic alkali, a process now known as *mercerization*. Mercerized fibers have a silken sheen and are quick to absorb dyes. The origin of plastic fibers also is associated with cotton. The first of these fibers was rayon, and later came the acetates. Both types are derived from *cellulose,* which is a substance that forms the walls of plant cells. This cellulose is first changed into a liquid, plastic material, which is then forced through tiny nozzles to produce the plastic fibers. Some years ago much of the cellulose used to make rayon came from cotton linters, but today forest products are largely drawn upon for making cellulose fibers.

Another plastic substance also had its origin in some 1868 experiments with cotton. A printer, who was trying to find an inexpensive material for making billiard balls, treated cotton linters with nitric and sulfuric acids to obtain nitrocellulose, which is the main ingredient of celluloid, a plastic that had very extensive use around the turn of the century. In more recent times, the treatment of cotton fiber with nitric and sulfuric acids has been widely employed in making guncotton, which is a military explosive.

Flax and the Linen Fabrics.   Flax is a plant that was known to the stone age men of Europe, and the ancient Egyptians used its fibers to make fabrics. The cultivated species is *Linum usitatissimum,* and presumably it was first raised in or near the Mediterranean area. Its stems contain long vascular bundles, which are stronger and more durable than cotton fibers, and are employed to manufacture the various types of linen that we use today. Another type of flax is grown largely for its seed.

Flax will prosper in both semitropical and temperate areas, and it has been a favorite fiber plant in northern Europe and Asia throughout historical time. It was brought to North America in colonial days, and we still raise some flax in the United States, but now it is largely of the type known as seed flax. Seeds from this flax are a source of industrial oil.

To free their fibers, flax stems are put through a "retting" process. There are various ways of doing this, and one of them is to keep bundles of stems underwater, and allow bacteria of decay to carry on their activities for a time. Fibers in the stems are partially freed in this process, and afterwards hand labor and machines are used to complete the job. Some flax fibers are as much as three feet in length, and can be used to manufacture cord or fabric of unusual strength. Yet, because the production of linen fabrics is more costly, flax ranks behind cotton as a source of fiber.

Hemp, Fiber, and Hashish. A number of different fiber plants are called "hemp," but the true hemp plant is *Cannabis sativa,* and the Chinese were cultivating it many years before the Christian Era. In fact, this species, which presumably was native to Asia, had reached Europe 35 centuries ago. True hemp belongs to the mulberry family; on the other hand, manila hemp comes from a member of the banana tribe, and an Asiatic favorite called sunn hemp is a legume plant.

Hemp is an annual herb that may attain a height of 15 feet, and produces seeds that are eagerly sought by various species of wild birds. The seeds also are a source of commercial oil in some parts of the world. Long fibers are obtained from hemp stems, following a retting process very similar to that employed in obtaining fibers from flax. Since a good deal of hand labor is required, hemp tends to be raised where such labor can be obtained at low cost.

But hemp may be found growing not only in Asia, but in Europe, North America, and South America as well. It was brought to the United States in pioneer days, and at times has been raised quite extensively in the Midwest. Here it often escapes from cultivation, and clumps of hemp plants are found growing wild in the pastures. The fibers are used to make cord, rope, coarse fabrics, and carpets.

In Asia, true hemp sometimes is raised primarily as a drug plant. A resinous gum from its flower tops contains cannabin, which is a narcotic that has been used for its pain-relieving effects. But the Asiatics also eat or smoke the gum resin, which they call hashish. Marijuana is another product which comes from the tops of wild hemp plants. The danger of using marijuana relates to the fact that the user may commit a crime while under its influence, and the possibility that he will "graduate" to the use of heroin.

Manila hemp comes from *Musa textilis* and related species, which are relatives of the bananas and plantains. These plants are native to southeastern Asia, the East Indies, and the Philippines, where natives have used them as a source of fiber for centuries. In modern times, *Musa textilis* was established in Central America. Manila hemp fibers are long and strong, and they come from the plant leaves. They are commonly used to make heavy rope, cord, or twine, and coarse types of paper.

A Fine but Strong Fiber. Fine fibers, yet strong fibers that will not shrink or stretch are supplied by the ramie plant (*Boehmeria nivea*). Ramie fibers are employed in making thread, fabrics, paper, and many other things.

Otherwise known as Chinese grass, the ramie plant is another Asiatic species, and the Orientals learned to use its fibers centuries ago. Undoubtedly it would have become highly popular had it not been for the fact that much hand labor was necessary to remove the fibers from the ramie stems. In recent times, however, machines have been invented to harvest the plants and peel off the outer bark of the stems. We may hear more about the ramie plant in years to come. It is now grown on an increasing scale in our southern states.

Jute for Burlap. Jute fiber is a material often used to make sacks, burlap bags, and other containers. Jute plants belong to the genus *Corchorus* of the basswood or linden family, and they are annuals. Their fibers, which come from the stems, are not particularly strong, but they spin readily and generally are available at moderate cost.

Jute plants have been cultivated for a long time, and probably are native to the southeast Asian area. They are still raised extensively in India, and to some extent in both North and South America. The fibers are retted out of the stems, and in addition to burlap, are employed to make other coarse fabrics, twine, and carpets.

Sisal for Cord and Rope. The ancient Aztecs made use of fibers from sisal plants of the genus *Agave*, and this practice has been continued and extended. Agave fibers have now become an important world commodity. Sisal plants are perennials, and they are now grown in various parts of the world, including Mexico, Central America, the West Indies, Hawaii, and Africa.

One special virtue of sisal plants is that they will prosper on dry soil, so they may be raised where many other crop plants would wither and die. The commercial fibers are obtained from their leaves, and are largely used to produce various types of cord and rope (Fig. 5-2).

Kapok for Upholstering and Pillows. Plant fibers also find extensive use in providing packing and stuffing materials. Such materials come from many different sources, and one of them is the kapok tree, *Eriodendron anfractuosum*, which appears to have been native to tropical America, but is also to be found today in Africa and southern Asia.

Kapok trees are fairly large and produce their seeds in pods. The commercial fibers are attached to these seeds. Lacking twist, these fibers are not of value for spinning yarns, but they

Fig. 5-2. Sisal plants with their upright, bladelike leaves growing in East Africa. Sisal is one of the world's important fiber plants.

are often used to stuff upholstered furniture, mattresses, pillows, and life preservers.

Fabrics from the Bark of Trees. All of the fabrics we have mentioned so far are produced by spinning and weaving. But some fabrics, such as tapa cloth, are simply made from the bark of a tree. The tapa cloth tree is *Broussonetia papyrifera,* a mulberry family species found in Asia and on islands of the South Seas. Natives of these areas have used tapa cloth very extensively in the past.

To make tapa cloth, strips of inner bark, which contain many fibers, are laid on a smooth surface with their margins overlapping. Then the mass is pounded with a mallet until it becomes a continuous sheet of material, which may be thin or thick, depending upon what is desired. This sheet of material can now be used to fashion various garments. Similar bark fabrics are made by natives in other parts of the world.

Fibers for Many Purposes. By this time the reader must be aware that commercial fiber is found in a great many plants belonging to a wide range of plant families. In these pages, we have "merely scratched the surface." There are, for example, a number of fibers used in making straw hats, all sorts of fibers that are employed to make baskets, fibers that we see in many varieties of brooms and brushes, and fibers that are used to caulk boats. There are also many fibers that are converted into paper, but these are discussed in Chapter 6.

Some Plant Oils

Mention has already been made of plant oils, and especially those derived from olives and coconuts (see Chapter 3). People of the old world have used certain plant oils for centuries, especially in the Mediterranean area. In our own country, there was little tendency to make use of the plant food oils until the latter part of the nineteenth century. Prior to that time, American food fats came largely from animal sources.

But now the wheel has turned, and in modern American markets oils from plant sources have largely displaced the once-familiar jars and cans of lard, and butter substitutes vie with butter for public favor. The plant oils have meanwhile become of vast importance in world economy, some of them being employed largely as food oils, others as industrial oils, and some for both purposes.

Cottonseed Oil and Cotton By-products. Until about 1860, cottonseed was merely a waste product of the cotton industry. To be sure, oil had been extracted from cottonseed way back in the eighteenth century, but there were no mills to do this job on a commercial scale. But now mills that could express oil from cottonseed came into existence, and samples of their products went out to various parts of the world.

Before long olive oil producers along the Mediterranean shore discovered that they could mix olive oil and the less expensive cottonseed oil to yield a product that would serve in cooking and in salads. Sardine canners found that their tiny fish could be packed in cottonseed oil. Soap manufacturers began to use cottonseed oil as one of their raw materials. Manufacturers of early butter substitutes learned that cottonseed oil would also serve their purposes. So the uses of the new product began to expand, and this trend has never been halted, although special taxes to discourage the use of margarines were imposed in some states for long periods of time.

We also use cottonseed oil in manufacturing various other products today, including roofing materials, putty, glycerine, and explosives. In a recent year, American production was over 3½ billion pounds of crude and refined oil, and only soybean oil was produced in greater quantity.

In addition to containing oil, cottonseed has other good qualities. The seed coats or hulls can be used as stock food and in fertilizers, or processed to obtain sugar, alcohol, and explosives. The fuzzy short hairs or linters are a source of industrial cellulose and of all sorts of stuffing materials. After the oil has been expressed from the hulled seeds, the residue is a cottonseed meal or cake, which also can be fed to livestock or used as fertilizer. Even the stalks of cotton plants have a potential value, since they contain fiber suitable for making paper.

So the cottonseed that was once discarded is in demand today, to the extent that some cotton growers raise varieties that lack staples for the most part, but produce a good yield of seed. In a recent year, commercial cottonseed production in this country was nearly 6 million tons; meal and cake production was about 2½ million tons; about 1⅛ million tons of hulls were made available; and over 1½ million bales of linters were taken from the seeds.

Soybean Oil and Related Products. The status of the soybean as a food plant has been discussed in Chapter 3, but modern exploitation of this species is not limited to using its seeds as a food product. There are at least two general methods of extracting oil from soybean seeds, and the residue or meal also has significant uses in modern economy.

Soybean oil, like cottonseed oil, serves both as a food material and as an industrial substance. Some of it is refined and incorporated in salad oils, cooking oils, and butter substitutes. The rest of it goes into a long list of materials that includes paints, soaps, candles, glycerine, explosives, and rubber substitutes. Soybean meal is a source of flour, and may be fed to livestock or used in compounding fertilizers. This meal has a high protein content, and from the protein come adhesives, such as those used to bond together the thin sheets that make up plywood. Soybean adhesives are particularly good for this purpose because they are relatively waterproof. Soybean protein enters into the manufacture of many plastic products that appear in our automobiles, airplanes, radios, and various fixtures about the home. It seems probable that the soybean is destined to play a role of increasing importance in human affairs.

In a recent year, nearly 5 billion pounds of crude soybean oil were produced in the United States, and another 4 billion pounds of refined soybean oil. This makes a total of 9 billion pounds; far more than the production of any other plant oil. In terms of domestic output, the leading plant oils discussed in this chapter rank in the order of soybean oil, cottonseed oil, corn oil, linseed oil, and peanut oil.

Oils from Corn, Peanuts, and Similar Sources. A good

deal of the cooking oil we use today comes from seeds of the corn plant. Like cottonseed and soybean oil, corn oil has other uses related to industrial production. Peanuts are another common source of vegetable oil, which is used as a cooking or salad oil, in butter substitutes, and in manufacturing soaps and machine oils. United States production of corn oil was over 700 million pounds in a recent year, and the corresponding figure for peanut oil was 125 million pounds.

Even the seeds of the sunflower plant, *Helianthus annuus*, have proved to be a fertile source of food oils and oils that can be used for various industrial purposes.

In some parts of the world, large amounts of vegetable fat are extracted from the nuts of the oil palm, *Elaeis quineensis*. This tree is native to tropical Africa, but has been introduced in the warm countries around the world. The oily product, like others previously discussed, serves both as a food and an industrial oil.

Linseed Oil and Tung Oil. Linseed oil and tung oil come from quite different sources, but they are both so-called drying oils and find similar uses in modern technology. Linseed oil is derived from seeds of the flax plant, whereas tung oil comes from seeds of tung trees, which are native to the Orient and belong to the genus *Aleurites* (Fig. 5-3).

Flax seeds have a relatively high oil content, and the linseed oil that comes from them is extensively used in paints, varnishes, and printer's ink. It also is employed in manufacturing linoleum, oilcloth, patent leather, and soft soaps. Linseed oil or cake ordinarily becomes food for livestock. In a recent year, United States production of flax seed was almost 32 million bushels. About 380 million pounds of raw and boiled linseed oil were made available.

Prior to about 30 years ago, there were no tung trees in North America, but subsequently plantings have been established in a number of southern states, and American tung oil production is increasing. Tung oil is particularly desirable for printer's inks and certain paints, but also is used in producing linoleum, oilcloth, soap, and other articles of commerce.

U.S.D.A. photo
Fig. 5-3. This planting of tung trees is eleven years old. Notice that the trees were in flower at the time this picture was taken.

The Volatile Oils. There are many other plant oils of greater or lesser importance in the modern scheme of things. Some of them are discussed in Chapter 6 because they have their origins in forest products. But in addition, there are various volatile or essential oils that come from representatives of many different plant families.

Volatile oils are aromatic, generally pleasing to the taste, and as the name indicates, they evaporate upon contact with the air. They are obtained from plant parts such as flowers, fruits, stems, leaves, or roots by simple expression in some cases, by distillation in others, or by using solvents. We produce some volatile oils in this country, but more commonly depend upon imports for the supplies required by American industries.

Some representative volatile oils that come from various herbs, shrubs, and trees are attar of roses, calamus oil, camphor, cananga oil, carnation oil, geranium oil, jasmine oil, lavender oil, lemon grass oil, neroli oil, oil of citronella, peppermint oil, rosemary oil, sandalwood oil, and wintergreen oil. Some of these oils, as well as others of similar nature, are used very extensively in manufacturing a variety of modern products which include such things as deodorants, flavoring substances, insect repellents, medicines, perfumes, and scented soaps.

The Tobacco Plants

Tobacco plants were known to the ancient Incas, who powdered dried tobacco leaf and used it as a drug in the treatment of head colds. Various wild tobaccos were native to tropical America, and the use of tobacco leaves apparently spread through ancient new world kingdoms in prehistoric times.

When Europeans reached eastern North America they found Indian tribesmen raising *Nicotiana rustica*, and smoking dried tobacco leaf. Smoking the "pipe of peace" figures largely in tales of the old frontier. But not all of the Indians confined their use of tobacco to smoking on ceremonial occasions; in fact, some of them chewed tobacco and used snuff. Various Europeans soon adopted these Indian practices, and proceeded to smoke and chew tobacco leaf whenever the spirit moved them. They also carried tobacco and the newly acquired habits back to Europe, where they were roundly condemned by some people and applauded by others.

Meanwhile farmers in the southern colonies began to raise *Nicotiana rustica*, but soon transferred their attentions to another and larger species, *Nicotiana tabacum*, which had been taken to Europe and then brought back to the colonies. The plant soon became a leading colonial crop because a ready market for the product had developed in the old world.

For a time, tobacco leaf even served as a sort of legal tender.

Modern Tobacco Plants. Despite opposition on moral grounds, heavy taxation, and other deterrents, men were soon smoking and chewing tobacco products throughout the world. Tobacco raisers began to develop special varieties, including some that could be raised in colder areas, and there are hundreds of these varieties in production today.

The tobacco plant is, of course, a member of the nightshade family, along with potatoes, tomatoes, eggplants and red peppers. It is an annual that is produced from seeds. The seeds are sprouted in beds, and young plants are subsequently set out in rows. Some types whose leaves are used to make cigar wrappings are grown under cloth. After a time, the tops of the plants are generally cut off, to concentrate growth in the

American Tobacco Co.

Fig. 5-4. Cultivating a tobacco patch on a small farm.

leaves. In harvesting, the leaves are either taken off separately, or entire plants are cut off at the base. In either case, the leaves are permitted to dry naturally, or are dried by controlled application of heat. Now the leaves may be piled up to ferment for a period of time, after which they are graded and aged.

In processing tobaccos, it is necessary to keep the moisture content at the proper level. For many kinds of tobaccos, flavoring materials such as rum, molasses, and sugar are added, and different varieties of tobaccos are often blended. For instance, tobaccos from foreign sources are used in producing the special blends of some American cigarettes.

Modern Uses of Tobacco. The modern equivalent of the Indian's pipe is still with us, and now and then people who chew the weed are found, although the once familiar brass cuspidor has all but vanished from the contemporary scene. People with the snuff habit also appear to be a declining group.

But this does not mean that world demand for tobacco products is waning. It merely indicates that times and customs have changed somewhat. The pipe came first, and it was followed by cigars which were very popular during the past century. Toward the end of this century, however, cigarettes began to appear in the marketplaces, and soon developed a following which does not appear to be greatly deterred by the threat of lung cancer or heart disease.

In a recent year, American tobacco growers produced over $2\frac{1}{4}$ billion pounds of tobacco, which was about one-fourth of the world crop. In the same year, American tobacco manufacturers turned out about 71 million pounds of smoking tobacco, 32 million pounds of scrap, 3 million pounds of fine cut, 26 million pounds of plug, 3 million pounds of twist, 33 million pound of snuff, $6\frac{1}{2}$ billion cigars, and 535 billion cigarettes.

Latex for Rubber

Rubber is another commodity that had its early beginnings in tropical America. The ancient Aztecs, Mayans, and Incas all possessed crude rubber, derived from the *latex* of certain forest trees. Spanish explorers found Central American natives playing a game in which a latex ball was used. These natives had even devised special paved courts upon which their games were conducted.

Crude rubber was carried back to Europe, but its real potentialities remained dormant for many long years. The main problem was the reaction of crude rubber to temperature changes. When it was warm it was likely to be a sticky mess, and when it was cold it became hard and brittle. In such variable form it was unsatisfactory for waterproofing garments, although this was attempted, or for much of anything else.

And so matters rested until 1839 when Charles Goodyear heated some crude rubber and sulfur together and discovered his vulcanizing process. The product was elastic, and happily it remained in the same state whether the winds blew hot or cold. Now for the first time the rubber industry was on its way, and improvements in the Goodyear process were made as time went by.

At first, sources of latex were limited to natural stands of trees in the tropical American jungles, but as rubber products became more and more in demand, it was obvious that extensive and stable sources of supply were required. Such sources, however, were not provided until the twentieth century was underway.

Rubber from Many Sources. Most of the rubber used today in making tires, waterproofing clothing, and in a thousand other things comes from cultivated varieties of *Hevea brasiliensis*, which was native to the Amazon Valley. This tree belongs to the spurge family of plants. But the reader should not suppose that *Hevea* is the only latex producer. In fact, natural rubbers can be obtained from quite a few tropical and semitropical plants, and some of these plants are not even closely related to *Hevea*.

For example, Panama rubber comes from trees of the genus *Castilla*, which belongs to a different plant family than *Hevea*. A Russian species of dandelion has latex in its roots. Certain goldenrod plants are potential sources of rubber, and so is one type of milkweed. But *Hevea* overshadows all other rubber sources in modern world economy. Until World War I, supplies of latex came largely from wild trees; after that time, plantation rubber became more and more of a factor in world supply.

Origins of Rubber Plantations. In 1876, some *Hevea* seeds were taken from the Amazon Valley to England, where seedling trees were sprouted. The young trees were then conveyed to British possessions in southeast Asia, and later to Dutch plantations in the East Indies, and then on to the Philippines. On these Asian plantations, experiments were carried out to develop special varieties of the trees and to determine the best production methods. The trees prospered in their new surroundings, where they enjoyed relative freedom from diseases, and by 1939 the East Indian plantations supplied most of the natural rubber in world markets.

Meanwhile, after World War I, rubber plantations were established in Central America and in Brazil. But here the planters encountered grave difficulties, primarily in the form of a fungus disease that destroyed the young *Hevea* trees. Apparently, when the trees grew wild and were dispersed through their native jungles, at least some of them escaped infection. But when large plantings were attempted, the fungal parasite quickly spread through the groves.

So rubber production in the new world languished for a time, but interest in the venture was revived in the early days of World War II. When the Japanese overran British and Dutch plantations in the southeast Asian area, rubber supplies were reduced drastically, and it became apparent that something had to be done about the problem.

One reaction was to attempt the re-establishment of rubber plantations in Central America and northern South America. And now better procedures were followed in selecting suitable rootstocks and grafting disease-resistant varieties on them. As a result, natural rubber production became a reality, although meanwhile World War II had ended, and rubber supplies were again available in the Far East.

The Development of Elastomers. The supply requirements of World War II also expedited the development and
use of "artificial rubbers," more properly known as elastomers.
These materials are derived from such substances as coal,
petroleum, chlorine, and carbon. Thus if we go back far
enough, at least some of them have plant origins. World War
II factories for their manufacture were established in the
United States, and all sorts of uses have been found for them.
Many different types of elastomers are now available.

Sometimes we hear the question, "Are elastomers better
than natural rubber?" This is not a question we can readily
answer. We must first ask, "Better for what?" Because actually, the natural rubbers are superior for some uses, and the

United Nations

Fig. 5-5.   Collecting latex from a tapped rubber tree in Southeast
Asia.

elastomers are preferable for others. And meanwhile, new plastics keep appearing, and some of them will doubtless find uses that are now served by rubber compounds. Both natural rubber and the elastomers, however, are likely to remain in demand during the foreseeable future.

From Latex to Rubber. Latex is a milk-like fluid that can be obtained by tapping the outer bark of a *Hevea* tree. Generally, the tapping is begun when the tree is five to six years old. The latex is drained off into a cup that is left attached to the tree. A worker makes daily rounds to collect the latex, and to extend the incision in the bark of the tree so that more latex will flow. This process is continued for a time, and then the tree is given a "rest."

When latex is exposed to air, the rubber material in it tends to coagulate, but this can be prevented by adding certain chemicals, whereupon the raw latex may be shipped in liquid form.

Natives of the Amazon Valley developed a primitive method of obtaining crude rubber from latex many years ago. They simply put the latex in a pot, and stirred it with a paddle. Some of the crude rubber stuck to the paddle, which was then held over a slow fire to speed coagulation. Then the paddle went back into the latex pot for another rubber coating, and so on until a mass of crude and partially solidified rubber was accumulated. The old Para rubber from the South American jungles was obtained in this manner.

In the case of modern plantation rubber, the story is somewhat different. Chemicals may be used to coagulate the crude rubber, which is then washed, rolled into sheets, and prepared for shipment. Or latex is simply shipped out in liquid form.

6

The Forests

Mankind has been associated with forests and their products for thousands of years. Forests provide materials that can be used to create shelters, and once man discovered how to control fire and cook some of his foods, he naturally depended upon trees to supply most of the fuels. Even before this time he had learned to forage in the forests for plant foods.

But stone age man would be astonished to see the array of products that come from the forests today. In addition to the familiar lumber and the fuels, we obtain such items as acids, adhesives, alcohols, animal foods, antifreeze compounds, clothing, dyes, disinfectants, elastomers, explosives, insulation materials, oils, papers, paints, photographic film, plastics, medicines, roofing materials, soaps, soil conditioners, rosin, solvents, stains, tannins, turpentines, sugars, veneers, and wallboard. About 4500 different manufactured products come wholly or in part from the forests.

In approaching this subject, we should note that there are three general types of forests that become established at the ends of long successions during which various plants and ultimately the trees compete with one another. In the end, certain dominant species of trees survive. First, there are *coniferous forests* or *softwood forests,* in which the dominant types are such trees as pines, spruces, hemlocks, firs, and redwoods. Such forests are best represented in Canada, Alaska, the Rocky Mountain area, and northern Asia. Second, there are *deciduous forests* or *hardwood forests,* made up of broad-leaved trees, such as our own elms, oaks, hickories, and maples. But we soon discover that tropical hardwood forests are very different from the hardwood forests of the United States. Temperate deciduous forests are located in various parts of the old and

new world, including an area in the eastern part of the United
States. Tropical hardwood forests are far more extensive, and
are best represented in Central America, tropical South America, tropical Africa, and the southeast Asian area including the
East Indies. The land that is most heavily forested probably
is New Guinea. Finally, there are *softwood-hardwood forests*
here and there, in which we find a mixture of conifers and
broadleaf trees.

Somewhat less than one-fourth of the earth's land surface
is forested today, since forests have been cut away in various

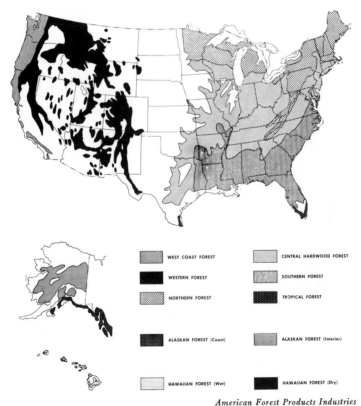

American Forest Products Industries

Fig. 6-1.   Forest regions of the United States.

heavily populated areas to make way for cultivated plants. The original forests of China, England, and much of southern Europe have been greatly reduced in extent. In our own country, more than half of the area originally in forests is still forested.

If we were asked to rank Africa, Asia, Europe, North America and South America with reference to the percentage of land that is forested, how would we do it? The correct answer is that the highest percentage of forested land is in South America, followed in order by Europe, North America, Asia, and Africa. We may think of Africa as a land of tropical rivers and jungles, and so it is in part, but Africa has vast tracts that are either grasslands or deserts.

Forests of the United States

Figure 6-1 shows the natural distribution of forests in the United States. The *northern forest* covers portions of New England, New York, Pennsylvania, Michigan, Wisconsin, and Minnesota, and extends southward from Pennsylvania along the Appalachian highlands. Pines, spruces, firs, hemlock, cedars, aspens, beech, birches, oaks, ashes, black cherry, linden, and black walnut may be found in various portions of this forest.

The *southern forest* extends along the South Atlantic and Gulf coast lines from Virginia to Texas, and northward along the Mississippi River to Missouri. In different parts of this forest are various types of pines, oaks, cypress, gum trees, hickories, pecans, ashes, poplars, and cottonwoods. Note in Figure 6-1 that a small area at the southern end of Florida bears a *tropical forest,* containing bay trees, mangroves, and mahogany.

The *central hardwood forest* lies more or less between the northern forest and the southern forest, and extends westward along various watercourses to reach eastern Nebraska, Kansas, Oklahoma, and Texas. Many portions of this forest have, however, been cleared away to provide fields for crops. The tree population includes maples, oaks, beech, hickories, elms, ashes,

Fig. 6-2. Some jungles look like this central American example and others do not. But you generally have to cut your way through the undergrowth.

gum trees, walnuts, tulip trees, sycamores, poplars, cotton-woods, and occasionally pines and cedars.

The *western forest* is best represented in the Pacific Northwest, but scattered portions appear in California, Nevada, Arizona, New Mexico, Colorado, Utah, Wyoming, and South Dakota. This is a forest dominated by pines, spruces, firs, and cedars, with broadleaf trees represented by the aspens.

The *west coast forest* lies along the coast line from Washington to about the middle of California, and features such trees as firs, hemlocks, pines, redwoods, cedars, maples and alders.

Forest Reserves and Forest Management. The relative importance of these American forests and their products has, of course, changed as the pioneers moved westward to occupy more and more territory. Today, most of our lumber comes from the west coast, western, and southern forests, with the northern forest and central hardwood forest making modest contributions. The bulk of our pulpwood comes from the southern forest, with smaller yields from the northern and west coast forests, and still less from the central hardwood forest.

States which have the largest amounts of sawtimber at the present time include Alaska, California, Idaho, Montana, Oregon, and Washington. Naturally, we find great differences among the 50 states; over 80 per cent of Maine is forested, whereas only 1 per cent of North Dakota is covered by trees.

Someone has said that it would have been better had North America been settled via the Mississippi Valley rather than the "stern and rockbound coast" of the Pilgrims. And certainly, there is some truth in the suggestion, because the eastern pioneers had to clear away the forests by cutting and burning to create their fields; they often found the fields so full of rocks that farming became a backbreaking and unrewarding enterprise. Their successors, who moved west over the Alleghenies, made similar assaults upon the hardwood forests, but here they found soils that were highly productive.

But despite provisions that have been made for agriculture, some 785 million acres of forest lands remain in the United States today (including the forests of Alaska); and while some preferred trees are in short supply, we have now reached the point in good forest management at which more wood is being produced than is being cut and used. About 60 per cent of domestic forest lands are in private hands, 25 per cent in national and state forests, and the rest held by various wood-using industries. Officials of lumber and pulp companies have long since realized that their welfare is related to forest conservation, for the future of these companies depends in large degree upon their ability to maintain forests in a state of continuous production.

And so the days of wasteful forest destruction belong largely to the past. Tree farming has become an established feature of the economy, and thousands of these farms are now in existence. This is all to the good since the average American uses three times as much forest products as the average European. Paper alone is a big item, and here we are thinking not only of the paper in books and notebooks, but also of the many coarser types that are used to make wrapping paper and paper bags.

Good forest management provides for the cutting of trees when they have reached their peak growth, and before decay has set in to any notable extent. It also provides for the rapid growth of new trees and the protection of trees against forest insects, disease, and forest fires. One way to reforest an area is to let nature do the job, but today an increasing number of trees that have been sprouted in nurseries are planted by hand or by machines.

Forest Insects, Diseases, and Fires.   Forest trees must

Weyerhaeuser Timber Co.

Fig. 6-3. Tree products are sometimes floated to the mills when water-ways are available.

American Forest Products Industries

Fig. 6-4. A lookout tower and plane in a southern forest. The job is to locate the telltale smoke of fires before they get well started.

survive many adverse effects of climate, weather, and competition with other trees. They are also threatened by insects, diseases, and fires. Interestingly enough, the insects and diseases are related, because certain insects convey disease parasites from one tree to another. Some of the forest insects are leaf eaters and are capable of destroying trees if the insects are present in sufficient numbers. Other insects, including various beetles, are wood borers, and in some areas they do much damage. The tree diseases are caused by a host of bacteria, fungi, and viruses, and some of these diseases, like the chestnut blight, are capable of wholesale destruction. As matters stand today, insects and diseases probably do more quiet damage than is brought about by the more spectacular forest fires.

We are really only beginning to attack the forest insect and disease problem. Helicopters are being used to spray trees infested with leaf-eating insects. Insect-infested and diseased trees are being cut selectively to salvage materials that can still be used and to prevent further spread of contamination. Disease-resistant varieties of trees are being sought in some special cases.

A great deal of progress has been made by way of controlling forest fires, but they are still a major menace, capable of wiping out the trees and leaving the soil a charred, infertile waste in some cases. Today, the larger forests have lookout stations, and airplane patrols are maintained to locate fires in their initial stages so that fire-fighters may reach the scene with a minimum of delay. Fire breaks are cut through the forests to facilitate the work of fire fighting. In addition to what might be called standard fire-fighting procedures, helicopters are now used to bring in fire fighters and their equipment in areas where forest roads do not exist. These measures have paid off, and burned-over acreage has decreased markedly in the past 30 years.

If we ask the average person what causes forest fires, he probably will answer "lightning," "spontaneous combustion," or something of the sort. But in reality, about 90 per cent of forest fires are due to human carelessness. There are indifferent campers who leave their fires untended, brush-burners who suddenly find that their fires have gotten out of hand, people who drop burning cigarettes on the dry forest floor, and believe it or not, some people who deliberately set fires. Most of these acts of human omission and commission are preventable, but of course there will always be some fires caused by natural agencies.

Pulp for Paper

No doubt most readers are aware that a good deal of the wood harvested today becomes wood pulp, and that much

Fig. 6-5.   Fighting a forest fire. A tractor and plow dig out a fire line, and a backfire is set up to create a burned-over area. If the onrushing fire does not cross this burned-over area, the fire may be brought under control.

wood pulp is used to make paper. There are two major substances in wood: one of them is the familiar cellulose, which is the same cellulose found in cotton or linen fibers. We use this wood cellulose to make paper, plastics, and many other things. The other main constituent of wood tissue is *lignin*, which used to be just a waste product in paper making, but now finds uses in the production of plastics, leathers, water softeners, and flavoring extracts. Together, cellulose and lignin make up about three-fourths of wood substance. The rest includes variable amounts of gums, minerals, oils, resins, sugars, and starches.

Early Writing Materials.   Before paper existed, men learned to use wood, stone, or clay tablets on which messages or records could be inscribed. At a later stage, they made sheets of parchment from the split hides of animals. The reason that college diplomas are sometimes called "sheepskins" is that many of them were once printed on parchment sheets.

In about 2400 B.C., the ancient Egyptians began to make *papyrus* by taking strips of fiber from stems of a Nile River plant, placing them in a criss-cross position, and applying weights until the fiber strips adhered to one another. Thus sheets of writing material were produced.

The Chinese began to make more modern types of writing materials in 105 A.D. These were really early types of paper; some being made from the fibers of mulberry bark, and others from silk fibers. Then the Arabs learned to manufacture paper from linen fibers, and brought this art to Europe in medieval times. Thereafter, various paper mills were established in Europe, and for a long time most of the paper was made from linen and cotton rags. But often such rags were not available in quantities that were large enough to meet existing demands, so the search for a cheaper and more abundant paper fiber continued.

Paper from the Trees. It was not until the nineteenth century, however, that the Europeans developed a successful method of making paper from wood pulp. Meanwhile, paper mills that used rags had operated in America for nearly 180 years. Now the first American pulp mill began to function in 1867. At this time, the demand for paper was still relatively modest, but a great change was in the making, and in a recent year American production of paper and paperboard was over 37 million short tons, of which over 16 million tons was paper rather than board. The vast bulk of this paper was made from wood pulp. Per capita use of paper and paperboard in the United States today is over 400 pounds per year. The average European gets along on far less, and in some parts of the world the average person uses only two or three pounds a year.

The first job in making paper from wood is to obtain the cellulose fibers. This is often done by cooking the wood in an alkali caustic soda solution (the soda process); or in sodium sulphide, sodium sulphate, and caustic soda (the sulphate process); or in a solution of acid calcium bisulphite (the sulphite process). The sulphate process was developed as a sort of afterthought, for dealing with wood that has a high resin content. A good deal of the product produced by the sulphate process becomes wrapping paper, but this process, like the other two, can also be employed to produce white papers.

In addition, wood from spruce trees is simply ground up to obtain a wood pulp that is used in making newsprint and wrapping papers. In this purely mechanical method, the lignin is not removed, and as a result, the product does not have good lasting qualities.

The particular method used, then, depends to some extent upon the type of paper to be made, and to some extent upon the wood to be processed. Papers for books and better grade magazines are often products of the soda process.

The wood pulp is now bleached and washed, and various substances such as clay, dyes, gelatin, and starch may be added, according to the type of paper desired. The resulting mixture of fibers and chemicals is picked up on a screen, which allows some of the liquid to run out of it, and then passes over a belt and through rollers, emerging as a flat sheet of paper. This paper is then dried, and may be further processed to give it a smooth surface.

Various types of spruce were once preferred for paper making, being relatively free from gums and resins; but other conifers such as pines, hemlocks, and firs, and deciduous trees such as maples, aspens, beech, alders, cherries, and birches are now used. In fact, almost any tree, as well as wood scraps, can now be employed to make pulp and paper. Some of the finer papers, however, still come from cotton and linen rags. At the other extreme, some cheaper and coarser papers are made from the stems of cereal grains, bamboo plants, and certain fiber plants such as hemp, ramie, and sisal. Old paper is also pulped, perhaps mixed with a certain amount of new pulp, and converted into paperboard.

Lumber and Plywood

Although we now use vast amounts of cellulose fiber to make papers and plastics, the majority of the trees harvested in the United States are destined to become lumber. This lumber is employed in construction work, and in making various types of furniture, as well as numerous fixtures and implements that we use in everyday life.

The softwood or coniferous trees contribute most of the lumber for building houses. Some of the hardwood or deciduous trees provide such items as flooring, as well as lumber that is extensively used in cabinet making. About 100 species of trees in the United States are potential sources of lumber, but only about 30 of these species make a substantial contribution to current lumber supplies. Most of our native lumber now comes either from privately owned or industry-owned lands; a much smaller amount is derived from the national forests.

Modern Harvesting and Processing Methods. Various methods are employed in harvesting tree crops. One of them is known as *selective cutting,* which is simply a matter of harvesting mature trees throughout an area and leaving the younger trees to provide similar crops in future years. Another method is called *block cutting.* In this process, a limited "block" or area within a forest is selected for harvesting. Necessarily, it is a block in which most of the trees have attained mature status. Trees in this area are harvested, although some of the smaller ones may be left standing to serve as "seed trees." In any event, the cleared area is limited in size, lies within the forest, and is likely to be re-seeded within a reasonable time by the surrounding forest trees. However, in some cases, we do not depend upon natural processes to re-seed an area. Helicopters are being used to spread fir seeds over some newly cut areas to speed up the process of tree replacement.

In harvesting, power saws are used to fell the trees. Their branches are then removed, and the trunks are cut into suitable lengths known as sawlogs. The sawlogs are transported to a sawmill, which is likely to be in the near vicinity.

At the sawmill, power-driven saws cut out the rough or unfinished planks and beams. Since the wood is green and subject to warping, it is now sorted out and stacked in sheds until it has dried, or the process is expedited by kiln drying. Finally, the rough lumber goes to the planing mill, where it is cut to desired sizes and shapes, and planed so that its surfaces are smooth.

The so-called veneers are thin slices that are cut out of some types of lumber. Sheets of veneer are commonly glued to the outer surfaces of cabinets that have been made from some less expensive types of wood. This art of veneering is anything but new. Egyptians were at least attempting it in about 1500 B.C.

Slices of veneer are also employed to make plywood. This is done by coating sheets of veneer with an adhesive, and then making a "sandwich" out of them, so-arranged that the grain of one sheet is at right angles to the grain of the adjoining sheets. Now the "sandwich" is put into a press, and heat and pressure are applied until the adhesive has hardened. The result is a sheet of wood material that has unusual strength. Plywoods with plain wooden cores or with particle board cores are also manufactured.

Many large structural pieces, or laminated beams, are made in similar fashion. In this case, powerful adhesives are used to bond together the smaller pieces of lumber that make up the beam. Again, the product has unusual strength in terms of its weight, and it can be shaped to meet a variety of needs. Wood is even bonded to metal in the laminating process.

In the course of harvesting and processing, bark, chips, limbs, sawdust, and shavings are produced in considerable quantity. At one time, most of such material was discarded, but this is no longer the case. Such things as fertilizers, fuels, glues, particle board, paneling, plastics, and soil conditioners come from these by-products. If they are not too resinous, chips and sawdust wastes may be ground into tiny particles to produce *wood flour*, which has various industrial uses, including the manufacture of linoleum. Whereas approximately two-thirds of the substance of a tree was largely wasted only

Fig. 6-6. A giant sequoia in north California. This specimen is over 250 feet in height. Notice how it towers above the surrounding trees.

a few years ago, virtually all of it is put to good use today.

Some Representative Softwoods. In the space available, we must limit our discussion of the lumber types. As for conifers or softwoods, it seems reasonable to give some attention to the pines. In colonial days, large areas of the northern forest were covered by growths of the northern white pine, *Pinus strobus.* This is a tree that attains a height of about 200 feet, and yields a light, soft wood which has reasonably good lasting qualities. Some of the old furniture that has been handed down to us from colonial days is made of northern white pine. At the time when this tree was in abundant supply, its lumber was used for various construction purposes; but today most of it becomes paneling, cabinets, window sashes, and similar items, for the northern white pine has long ceased to be America's number one lumber tree.

The southern yellow pine, *Pinus australis,* from the southern forest, is the source of a heavier and stronger product that is often used to make boards, beams, and other members used in heavy construction. At present, it is one of the more important sources of native lumber.

The big tree or sequoia of the west coast forest is *Sequoia gigantea,* and it is included here not because it is an important source of lumber, but due to the fact that the trees are so long lived and attain such exceptional size. Some sequoias are 350 feet in height and are estimated to have lived for over 40 centuries (Fig. 6-6). Even so, they are challenged by a cypress tree in Tule, Mexico, which some experts believe to be much older. This cypress is only about 150 feet in height, but it measures over 100 feet around the base.

The redwood trees (*Sequoia sempervirens*) of the west coast forest are almost as large as *Sequoia gigantea,* and are believed to live for as much as 20 centuries. They are found in the coastal forests from southern Oregon to San Francisco Bay, and they are of economic interest because of the lumber derived from them. Unfortunately, there are not nearly so many redwood trees as we would like to have. The lumber is soft and light, but it is strong and endures contact with soil and water. It has been in demand for paneling, furniture

U.S. Forest Service

Fig. 6-7. Preparing to drop a Douglas fir tree in a north California forest. Douglas fir is one of the important American lumber trees.

manufacture, shingles, general construction, and many other special uses. If it were not for the fact that protected areas have been set aside, populations of redwood trees probably would be declining, although they do tend to perpetuate themselves by sending up numerous shoots from old stumps.

The Douglas fir tree, *Pseudotsuga taxifolia,* of the Pacific Northwest, like the southern yellow pine, is among the important sources of native, softwood lumber today (Fig. 6-7). Douglas fir grows to be about 200 feet high, and provides very satisfactory sawlogs. The wood is fairly strong and quite durable. Supplies come largely from forests in western Washington and Oregon. The lumber is used in construction, for flooring, and in making veneers.

Several species of spruce belonging to the genus *Picea* are commercially important trees in the northern and western forests. As previously noted, a good deal of spruce becomes wood pulp, but spruce trees are also an important source of lumber that is used in construction. Spruce trees are even raised on tree farms to supply the Christmas tree market.

Representative Hardwoods of the United States. Oaks are characteristic trees of the central hardwood forest, and some of them are found in the northern and southern forests as well. About two dozen North American species have commercial importance, and they may be divided into two groups: the white oaks and the red oaks. For making lumber, the white oaks are preferred, because the product is harder and stronger. The black oaks are members of the red oak group; so are the pin oaks, scarlet oaks, and willow oaks. The white oak group includes the white oaks, bur oaks, post oaks, and chestnut oaks.

Oak lumber is hard and durable. Anyone who has driven nails in oak knows that this is quite different than driving them in pine or spruce. But oak is fine for heavy construction work. It also is a favorite for flooring, paneling, furniture, barrel staves, and wooden parts of various machines.

The white oak tree, *Quercus alba,* may be taken as an example of this group. In times past, its lumber has been widely employed in constructing the hulls of ships. It is a sturdy forest tree, common in the central hardwood forest, and found as far west as Minnesota and Texas. Under favorable conditions, white oaks may rear their gnarled branches to a height of 100 feet.

Maple trees also are representative hardwoods. Several maple species, to be sure, provide a rather soft lumber of minor importance, and some of these trees, such as the silver maple and ash-leaved maple are commonly grown as shade trees on lawns and in parks. But the sugar maple, *Acer saccharum,* presents quite a different case. This maple is also commonly grown as a shade and ornamental tree. But its lumber, which is sometimes called hard maple, is not only hard, but also strong and fine grained, and is capable of taking a beautiful polish.

Hard maple lumber has been used extensively to produce furniture, paneling, and some types of flooring. It also is the source of veneers, and parts of hundreds of commercial products.

Sugar maples are found in the central hardwood forest and on northward into Canada. They grow as far west as the Mississippi Valley and as far south as Florida and Texas. The trees may attain a height of over 100 feet, and they tend to spread out laterally unless they are in dense forest stands of timber.

Some Tropical Hardwoods. The tropical hardwood forests constitute the most extensive forest reserves of the world. Some of them are *rain forests,* and others are simply tropical deciduous forests of at least three types: *monsoon forests, savannah forests,* and *thorn forests.*

Rain forests are found in areas where annual rainfall is high, in some cases 150 to 250 inches a year, although it may be as low as 75 to 100 inches a year. In these areas, there is no dry season; it is likely to rain almost any day. Some of the rain forests are really jungles, and anyone who ventures into them must literally cut his way through, due to the presence of vines and undergrowth. In other cases, the forest floors are relatively open and clear, providing free and easy passage. Rain forest trees bear leaves throughout the year. The rain forest of the Amazon Valley is particularly notable because of the large number of tree species it contains; this number is said to be in excess of 2500.

Tropical deciduous forests occur in areas where there is a dry season, and many of the trees shed their leaves at this time. Monsoon forests of the southeast Asian area are often jungle-like because growths of bamboo are present. The savannah forests, in areas of less rainfall, are likely to be quite open, with grasses growing between the trees. Thorn forests develop where rainfall is even more scanty.

One of the tropical hardwoods the reader doubtless has seen is mahogany. Most of it comes from the Spanish mahogany tree, *Swietenia mahogani*, which is native to the West Indies, and the more important species *Swietenia macrophylla*, which is native to Central America and northern South America. But there are other trees that yield lumber called mahogany, and even some trees in other plant families that are sources of wood designated as California mahogany, mountain mahogany, and Natal mahogany.

Mahogany lumber was conveyed to Europe at an early date, and used to make carved interior decorations and furniture. Such uses of this reddish-brown wood have continued to the present day, and have been extended to include veneers, plywood, and lumber used in fashioning many different products that range from boat hulls to caskets. Plantings of mahogany trees have been established in southern Asia.

In the southeast Asian area, including the Philippines, the teak tree, *Tectona grandis*, is one of the leading sources of lumber. The wood is hard and durable, and when used in construction has been known to retain its integrity for more than five centuries. Teak trees grow quite rapidly, a fact which has encouraged the establishment of plantings. In addition to general construction, teak lumber is used in the manufacture of boat hulls, flooring, and furniture.

Another wood from the American tropics is worth mentioning because it is so different from most commercial lumbers. This is balsa wood from the species *Ochroma pyramidale*. Balsa wood is extremely light because its tissues are filled with air spaces. It is therefore quite useful in making insulation materials, and in manufacturing life preservers and other items that are used in and about the water.

Other Forest Products

Up to this point we have been concerned largely with wood and wood fiber. Other forest products are, however, of considerable importance in our daily lives, and these include a group of chemical substances that are derived from trees.

Pitch, Turpentine, and Rosin. Oil of turpentine and *rosin* have many modern uses. A great deal of turpentine acts as a thinner in paints and varnishes, and as a solvent in certain industrial processes. Rosin, although less well known to the average person, is used to manufacture many things, includ-

U.S.D.A. photo

Fig. 6-8. In the southern forest, crude pine "gum" is collected from pine trees. This crude material is the source of turpentine and rosin.

ing adhesives, paints, paper, plastics, roofing materials, rubbers, and soaps.

Both of these substances are obtained by the destructive distillation of pine wood, but the more common source is the pitch or crude turpentine that is exuded by various conifers. This pitch is one type of *resin*. The favorite North American source is the southern yellow pine (*Pinus australis*) of the southern forest. Trees of this species are tapped, and the crude turpentine is allowed to run out into containers (Fig. 6-8). It is then distilled; and when the product settles, the liquid turpentine rises to the top and is removed. The residue cools, hardens, and becomes rosin. In a recent year, domestic production of turpentine was almost 33 million gallons, and the rosin yield was over 2 million 520-pound drums.

The Canada balsam that has been used so commonly to attach coverglasses to microscope slides is also a turpentine that is exuded by balsam fir trees. This balsam is also employed in compounding medicines, and in various industrial processes. Incidentally, the word "balsam" is misleading in this case, because so-called Canada balsam is not a true balsam. The true balsams are also tree products such as balsam of Peru and benzoin.

Resins for Varnishes and Lacquers. Members of a number of plant families produce hard resins, which often flow out through cracks in the bark and then harden when they come in contact with the air. For example, the reader may have heard of amber, which is a resin that was produced millions of years ago and became fossilized.

Resin is obtained in part by tapping certain forest trees, but also in some cases by collecting old deposits of resinous materials that have accumulated at or near the soil surface. Most of this hard resin comes from trees native to southeast Asia, the Philippines, Africa, Australia, and South America.

Hard resins dissolve in solvents such as alcohol, and some of them are used to make varnishes, while others serve to provide lacquers. The use of such substances to coat various articles antedates the Christian Era. Resins are also used in the manufacture of products such as inks, plastics, and soaps.

Tannins for Leather Manufacture. Apparently peoples of both the old and the new world learned to tan animal hides and produce leathers centuries ago. The substances and methods they used necessarily varied, and even today, there are a number of common procedures. They center, however, around the use of *tannins,* which are plant substances that unite with animal proteins, so that subsequently if the hides are worked as they dry, a flexible product results. Tannins find further utility in the manufacture of inks.

Many plants contain tannins, but some species contain far more than others. It has been suggested that these tannins represent waste products of plant metabolism. We naturally turn to the particular plants from which the largest amounts of tannins can be obtained. Commercial sources include various types of wood, bark, leaves, roots, and fruits. As far as native supplies are concerned, chestnut wood, hemlock bark, oak bark, and sumac leaves have all been used to a greater or lesser extent. An important exotic source is the wood of two South American trees known as quebrachos. These trees are members of the sumac family.

Cork and Cork Products. We take cork more or less for granted because it is a part of so many articles that we see and use every day. It may even form the corkboard that insulates the walls of our homes, or be present in the inner soles of our shoes. Most of this material represents the outer bark of the cork oak, *Quercus suber,* which is native to the Mediterranean area, including southern Europe and North Africa.

Cork oak trees continue to produce usable bark for many years. Layers of bark are removed from the mature tree trunks and branches about every eight years, boiled to remove unwanted chemical substances, and shipped to the markets. Cork oak trees are now being raised in warmer areas of our Southwest.

Cork cells are also found in the barks of some other tree species, although not as abundantly as in *Quercus suber.* Products similar to cork are derived from some of these trees.

Many articles are made directly from cork, but the scraps

and trimmings are not wasted. They are ground up, mixed with an adhesive filler, and pressed into sheets of material, which are used to make gaskets, bottle caps, floor coverings, and other useful articles.

Charcoal and Related Products. Charcoal largely consists of carbon. It has been used as a fuel for centuries, and it still serves this function in some parts of the world. A metal brazier filled with burning charcoal is often used to heat dwelling places. One good quality of charcoal is that it burns without producing much smoke. This is one reason why it has become popular with Americans who enjoy cookouts during the summer season. Charcoal is also used as a fuel in some blast furnaces, in filters of various types, and in some manufacturing processes.

The ancient way to produce charcoal was to pile wood on the ground or in pits, set it on fire, and partially cover it with earth. This practice is still followed in some parts of the world, and the forest huts of poor but honest charcoal burners continue to reappear in fictional tales. But the modern way to obtain charcoal is through the destructive distillation of wood, which has the advantage that it yields by-products in the form of wood tar, acetic acid, methanol, and methane.

Future Prospects

This is not a volume on conservation, but it is appropriate to note that many modern conservation practices have an intimate relationship to plant resources. With the human population increasing in a rather startling fashion, anything that contributes to the effectiveness of biological production is of practical value and concern.

We have seen how improved practices have led to the establishment of North American forests on a basis of continuing production. Various measures have made this possible, including better systems of harvesting forest products and increasing efforts to control forest insects, diseases that affect trees, and forest fires. In addition, forest areas are sometimes re-seeded, or seedling trees are set out in place of trees that have been felled. In fact, there is an increasing tendency to establish tree farms or plantations so that future supplies of desirable species may be available in greater quantity. Meanwhile, geneticists are at work on various problems relating to the development of special tree types.

When we look back upon the production of garden and field crops, the story is much the same. Of course the growing of field crops does introduce special problems of soil depletion and erosion to a greater extent than in the case of forests. But the same challenge to protect crop plants against hordes of hungry insects and disease-producing parasites exists. Certain mechanical, chemical, and biological controls are employed, and without them production would suffer both in quantity and in quality. In this case also, plant geneticists make a contribution by developing improved varieties of field and garden plants, which often means varieties that can survive the attacks of certain parasites.

We do not ordinarily think of water as something that is in short supply. Nevertheless, large tracts of desert and dryland exist in various parts of the world, including our own country. Many of these tracts are potentially productive, assuming that supplies of fresh water can be made available at reasonable cost. But up to now, water for irrigation has not been provided in a good many dryland areas. This is a problem for the future, and research designed to develop low-cost methods of desalinating sea water is in progress.

Bibliography

Buehr, Walter. *Timber! Farming our Forests*. New York: William Morrow and Co., 1960.

Cook, J. Gordon. *The Fight for Food*. New York: Dial Press, 1957.

Cromie, William J. *Exploring the Secrets of the Sea*. Englewood Cliffs, N.J.: Prentice-Hall, Inc., 1962.

Dodge, Bertha S. *Plants that Changed the World*. Boston: Little, Brown, and Co., 1959.

Fenton, Carroll L. *Plants That Feed Us*. New York: John Day Co., 1958.

Hibben, Frank C. *Digging up America*. New York: Hill and Wang, 1961.

Hyde, Margaret O. *Plants Today and Tomorrow*. New York: McGraw-Hill Book Co., 1960.

McCormick, Jack. *The Living Forest*. New York: Harper and Brothers, 1959.

Quinn, Vernon. *Leaves—Their Place in Life and Legend*. New York: Frederick A. Stokes Co., 1957.

Ray, Peter M. *The Living Plant*. New York: Holt, Rinehart and Winston, 1963.

Selsam, Millicent E. *How to Grow House Plants*. New York: William Morrow and Co., 1960.

Shannon, Terry. *The Wonderland of Plants*. Chicago: Albert Whitman and Co., 1960.

Sterling, Dorothy. *The Story of Mosses, Ferns, and Mushrooms*. New York: Doubleday and Co., 1955.

Symonds, George W. D. *The Tree Identification Book*. New York: M. Barrows and Co., 1958.

Watts, May T. *Reading the Landscape*. New York: Macmillan Co., 1957.

Glossary

Agar. A carbohydrate product obtained from certain red algae.

Algae. Several phyla of simple plants that live in water or moist places on the land. All of them are food-makers.

Annual. A plant which develops from a seed, flowers, fruits, and dies in the same season.

Antibiotic. A substance derived from molds or bacteria and which is used to combat diseases.

Bacteria. A group of single-celled plants that usually have no chlorophyll, and have no organized nuclei.

Biennial. A plant which arises from seed one year, lives to the next season, and then flowers, sets seed, and dies.

Carnivore. A flesh-eating animal.

Cellulose. A compound commonly found in the walls of plant cells.

Chemosynthesis. A type of food manufacture by certain bacteria in which necessary energy is derived from chemical sources rather than from sunlight.

Chlorophyll. Green-colored substances of plants which are essential if photosynthesis is to take place.

Colchicine. A drug derived from a member of the meadow saffron family.

Coniferous forests. Forests dominated by conifers such as pines, firs, and spruces.

Curare. A poisonous substance derived from plants of the genus *Strychnos.*

Deciduous forests. Forests dominated by deciduous plants, which shed their leaves seasonally.

Fungi. Various comparatively simple plants that have no chlorophyll, and live as parasites or saprophytes.

Hardwood forest. Forests dominated by deciduous trees such as oaks and maples.

Herbivore. A plant-eating mammal.

Latex. A product obtained from *Hevea* trees that is used to produce rubber.

165

Legumes. Members of a plant family which includes beans, soybeans, peanuts, peas, and lentils.

Lespedezas. Certain types of legume plants that are raised as forage crops.

Lignin. A substance found in plant cells.

Maize. Another name for Indian corn.

Molds. One group of fungi. Like other fungi, they are unable to make foods.

Mycelium. The underground structure from which a mushroom grows.

Nitrates. Nitrogen compounds which are essential to the growth of plants.

Omnivore. An animal that eats a variety of both plant and animal foods.

Papain. An enzyme derived from fruits of the papaya plant.

Parasite. An organism that lives at the expense of other organisms.

Perennial. A plant which lives for at least three or more years. Many tree species are perennials, and some of them live for hundreds or thousands of years.

Photosynthesis. A type of food manufacture in chlorophyll-bearing plants which utilizes the energy of sunlight.

Plankton. A floating mass of small organisms found near the surface of the sea or in bodies of fresh water.

Ramie. A fiber-producing plant from the Orient.

Resin. A substance formed in the tissues of various plants. Not to be confused with rosin.

Rosin. A commercial product obtained from crude turpentine or pitch.

Saprophyte. An organism that feeds upon dead plants, or animals, or both.

Sisal. A fiber obtained from plants of the genus *Agave*.

Symbiosis. A mutually beneficial relationship between two organisms.

Tannins. Substances found in many plants, which are used to manufacture leathers.

Tapa cloth. A fabric made from the bark of trees.

Truffle. A European type of fungus that is used to flavor foods.

Tung oil. A drying oil obtained from the seeds of tung trees.

Index

Holt Library of Science